THE DOLAUC

Geolog, ...ning History

(New Revised Edition)

THE DOLAUCOTHI GOLD MINES

Geology and Mining History

(New Revised Edition)

Alwyn E. Annels and Barry C. Burnham

With contributions by
Keith P. Williams, Peter J. Brabham and Alun K. Isaac

APECS Press
Caerleon

First Edition 1983
Second Edition 1986
Third Edition 1995

New Revised Edition published by APECS Press 2013

Editing and design by
APECS Press Caerleon

ISBN 978-0-9563965-5-6

The publisher gratefully acknowledges the financial support
of SRK Consulting (UK) Ltd.

Printed in Wales by
Dinefwr Press, Llandybïe, Carmarthenshire

To all those university staff and students from
Cardiff and Lampeter who contributed to the rehabilitation,
development and understanding of the Dolaucothi Gold Mines
and especially to the people of Pumsaint and district
who provided much appreciated and essential logistical support.

CONTENTS

LIST OF ILLUSTRATIONS

FOREWORD

Since the last edition of this book was published in 1995 there have been extensive additional studies of the Dolaucothi Mine undertaken by geologists, geochemists, geophysicists and archaeologists. As a result, this current edition represents a more detailed and comprehensive edition with much new information and interpretation. In addition, some of the previous black and white photographs and diagrams have been replaced by colour versions thus markedly enhancing the general presentation of the material included in the book.

Gold holds a fascination for many and this book provides the reader or visitor with a much more comprehensive account of this former gold-mining site, both from the point of view of its history and its geology. Included for the first time are details of geophysical and geochemical investigations which have informed an understanding of aspects of the early workings, tangible evidence for which has long been destroyed by later mining activities.

An extremely valuable comprehensive glossary is provided for the non-technical reader which is vital for non-experts who are trying to piece together a broad understanding of the mine contained within the information presented relating to mining techniques, mineral deposit features and geological terminology.

In summary it represents a very readable and significant contribution to the published literature on Roman and post-Roman mining in Wales, specifically in relation to gold, and highlights some of the areas where there remains either a lack of knowledge or controversy over interpretation.

Dr. Richard Bevins
Keeper of Geology
Amgueddfa Cymru-National Museum of Wales

May 2013

ACKNOWLEDGEMENTS

The authors would like to acknowledge the technical and financial contributions made by the University Colleges of Lampeter and Cardiff and also by the organisations and mining companies which supported the research into the history and geology of the Dolaucothi Gold Mines and which, in turn, formed the basis of the first three editions of this book. A list of these contributors appeared in the 1995 (Third) edition.

The current book is a heavily revised edition which has been made possible by the generous financial and moral support of SRK Consulting (UK) Ltd. In addition, particular acknowledgement is made of the assistance provided by Dr. Peter J. Brabham (Cardiff University) in the production of colour versions of some of the original illustrations and also new photographs and diagrams which greatly enhance the general presentation of the new book. Chapters 4 and 5 have benefited significantly from the advice and expertise of Mr. Robert Protheroe Jones (National Museum of Wales), who also provided access to additional historical information.

Thanks are also due to Dr. Richard E. Bevins (National Museum of Wales) for kindly providing us with a Foreword, to Mrs. Helen Burnham for putting the final touches to several of the illustrations and to Mrs. Margaret Isaac for reading and suggesting modifications to the text, from the point of view of the general reader.

Dr. Alwyn E. Annels
Professor Barry C. Burnham

July 2013

CHAPTER 1

INTRODUCTION*

The gold mines at Dolaucothi preserve for the visitor a wealth of surface and underground workings of the utmost importance, spanning as they do periods of exploitation potentially from the pre-Roman and Roman periods through to the 20th century. They are situated in south-west Wales, just off the A482 road from Llanwrda to Lampeter, about one kilometre south-east of the modern village of Pumsaint. The main workings can be traced over a distance of more than a kilometre, extending north-east to south-west along a mountain spur forming the south-eastern side of the Cothi valley (Figure 1.1 shows the 3D topographic relief in the vicinity of the mine and in particular the Cothi valley). The workings comprise a series of large opencast pits, trenches and underground galleries, several leats supplying water to a system of tanks and reservoirs, and the remains of various processing mills and their associated buildings. Today these features form part of a much more extensive estate extending over some 2,500 acres, which was given to the National Trust in 1941–1943 by Mr. H.T.C. Lloyd-Johnes, whose family is known to have owned

Figure 1.1: 3D topographic map of the Cothi Valley (P.J. Brabham, Cardiff University).

* For an explanation of technical terms see the glossary at the end of the volume.

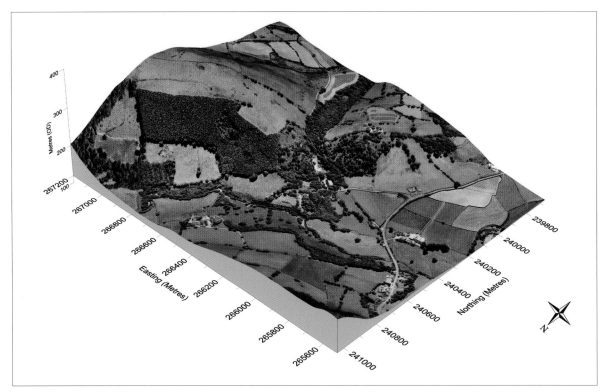

Figure 1.2: 3D topographic map of the mine workings centred on the Ogofau Pit at Dolaucothi
(P.J. Brabham, Cardiff University).

the land since the time of Henry VII. The present car-park, by which the visitor approaches the site, lies at the foot of the main focus of the workings known today as the Ogofau Pit. This is a large opencast situated in a saddle of land separating the higher ground of Allt Ogofau to the south-west from the prominent ridge of Allt Cwmhenog to the north-east (Figure 2.1, Area 4 and Figure 1.2).

The mine workings have been the source of increasing speculation and interest for over three centuries, since their first brief mention in the 1695 edition of Camden's *Britannia*. Somewhat more informative are the entries in a journal compiled by the naturalist, Sir Joseph Banks, dated 26th August 1767, which clearly mention a visit to one of the underground galleries on Allt Ogofau, most likely that now known as Upper Roman Adit (Figure 4.5). Both he and other antiquarian observers of the early 19th century were also well aware of the existence of an old watercourse or leat, which could be traced over a distance of some 11 kilometres from close to the source of the river Cothi to near the head of the workings (Figure 4.7), and of the Carreg Pumsaint which, even then, was recognised as a probable mortar stone, despite its local association with the legend of the 'Five Saints' (Figure 4.13). Already by this date there was a strong local tradition ascribing the workings to the Romans, a theory readily given credence by the discovery of a hoard of Roman gold jewellery, initially in 1796 or 1797 and subsequently added to in 1819, and by the rather haphazard 'excavation' of a probable bath-house in the 1830s south of the Cothi and west of the modern A482. There was little evidence, however, for the nature of the metal being sought. This was apparently only resolved in 1844, when Sir Warrington Smyth and members of the Geological Survey first recognised a speck of free gold in a fragment of the ubiquitous quartz found at the mines. Smyth it was, also, who published the first survey of the two adits now known to us as Upper and Lower Roman in 1846.

Perhaps the most significant of the early records of the mines is a series of topographical maps which were produced in 1868 by Sir John Gardner Wilkinson. Now housed in the Bodleian Library in Oxford, they have been the subject of recent study and a preliminary publication by C.S. Briggs. Some five plans have survived, including one master map which covers the full extent of the workings from north-east to south-west. Though a detailed assessment of their importance must await their full publication, they represent the earliest known topographical survey of the area, clearly depicting not just the mining landscape in its entirety but also many of the individual features which are of such importance to the archaeological study of the site. They are especially valuable because they depict the landscape before its extensive development as a working gold mine in the years after 1870. While these later mining operations often brought new information to light, they inevitably also added an element of complexity to the existing surface evidence, in some cases by destroying traces of earlier activity, in others by modifying or masking it.

The ancient workings were first systematically described by F.J. Haverfield and R.C. Bosanquet in the early 20th century (drawing extensively on an unpublished paper by Mr. Horace Sanders), at which time the chance was also taken to explore the line of the Cothi leat and one of the large tanks located along its course (Figure 4.1, Tank E). The possibility that some of the workings should be assigned to the Normans was tentatively advanced by Bosanquet, who pointed to the remains of a possible 'motte' above the workings on Allt Ogofau. Interest was further aroused during renewed mining operations in the 1930s, when tunnelling from the shaft at the entrance to the Ogofau Pit allowed access to a series of large underground galleries extending up to 44 metres below the surface (Figure 5.5). Here several well-preserved wooden objects were discovered by the miners, including a possible panning cradle (or shovel?), a ladder, various timber props and, most important of all, a fragment from the rim of a drainage wheel (now in the National Museum of Wales), of a type not dissimilar to a Roman example known from Rio Tinto in Spain (now in the British Museum). At the time, the leading authority on Roman mining, O. Davies, reaffirmed the view that the workings were essentially Roman in origin. Further fieldwork in 1959 confirmed the detailed line of the Cothi leat.

The most detailed investigations of the site were undertaken in the late 1960s and early 1970s, under the aegis of the Dolaucothi Research Committee of the National Museum of Wales, involving two separate, though interrelated projects: the first combined surface survey and selective excavation to elucidate, in particular, the history of Roman exploitation at the site, directed primarily by G.D.B. Jones and P.R. Lewis; the second saw an exploration of the accessible underground galleries, most of them of 19th- and 20th-century date, by the then Department of Mineral Exploitation, University College, Cardiff. The archaeological aspect of these investigations included the first truly systematic descriptions of the main surface workings, a further investigation of the Cothi leat, the discovery of the so-called Annell leat, running at a higher level above the workings, and the excavations within the recently discovered Roman fort beneath the modern village of Pumsaint. Parallel work in the mining areas of Roman Spain, especially in the vicinity of Las Medulas, also provided valuable comparative evidence of the importance of water in contemporary mining operations. This work provided the framework for a simple developmental model of Roman mining at Dolaucothi, the broad details of which continue to be rehearsed and debated in the archaeological literature.

Following this pioneering research there was a lull in the pace of archaeological activity until renewed operations began in 1982 under the aegis of the then Archaeology Unit (later the

Department of Archaeology) at Lampeter. This led to the identification of a possible water-driven mill complex and its associated features in 1982, the recording of the exposed archaeological section south of the fort in 1985, and limited survey work on Upper and Lower Roman Adits in 1986, prior to their being lit and opened to the public.

Such small-scale interventions paved the way for a more concerted programme of work between 1987 and 1999, directed by B.C. Burnham and H.B. Burnham. This sought to investigate several aspects of the workings and their associated features (for the location of the sites, see Figure 4.1): in 1989, following trial work in 1987, large-scale excavations were undertaken in the north-west part of the fort at Pumsaint; in 1990, survey and small-scale trenching examined the Upper Annell and Gwenlais leats (the latter a new discovery by D. Bick in 1988); in 1993, this work was extended to the terminus of the Annell leat and the associated Tank (G) above the Allt Cwmhenog Pit; in 1991–93, excavations near the entrance to the Ogofau Pit investigated a series of processing wastes in the vicinity of the postulated mill complex (Figure 1.3); in 1997, trial excavations and geophysical survey explored the line of the Roman road from Llandovery to Pumsaint and an area of related settlement west of the presumed site of the 'bath-house'; finally, in 1997 and 1999, geophysical survey examined the east side of the fort, together with an area of associated settlement (this latter area was further extended in 2011 to complete the geophysical coverage of virtually all the accessible areas in and around the fort). The results of this extensive programme have now been fully published (see Burnham & Burnham 2004 in the selected references at the end of the volume).

Other recent work at the mines has included a detailed survey of the surface workings, together with an appropriate overlay of archaeological interpretation, undertaken by Cambria Archaeology in 1999 and 2002, and a short season of survey on both the surface and underground workings

Figure 1.3: Excavations in progress on the processing wastes, 1993 (B.C. Burnham).

by a Franco-British team led by B. Cauuet in 2000. These latter activities pose interesting questions which only further excavation will resolve.

Despite the lull in archaeological work during the later 1970s, geological research continued apace. In 1974, geological staff of the Department of Mineral Exploitation, University College Cardiff, began a detailed geological survey of the site which resulted in the production of both surface and underground maps and led to a greater understanding of the nature of the main types of gold mineralisation present and their possible mode of origin. This work stimulated more detailed research into this unique occurrence of gold and also led to the realisation that the mine had tremendous potential as a focus for undergraduate and postgraduate research and practical training.

In 1978, therefore, the Department of Mineral Exploitation decided to rehabilitate and develop the mine workings into a Mining Field Centre at which students following degree courses in mining geology, mining engineering and minerals processing could gain valuable experience and also develop the skills necessary to work in integrated multi-disciplinary teams. A successful application was thus made to the National Trust for a 21-year lease of access to the workings and to the Crown Estate Commissioners for a similar lease to the underground workings. The latter allowed limited production of gold-bearing ore for educational and research purposes only.

The first task was to rehabilitate those workings which were relatively accessible and to establish surface infrastructure (e.g. a mine office) from which the work could be coordinated. This work was largely completed by 1983 and involved a number of basic operations centred on the workings associated with Mitchell, Long and Mill Adits (Figure 5.2), which included the clearance of underground entries and the installation of gateways, the clearance of collapsed rock and rotten mine timbers and the re-support of the roof, the improvement of drainage systems and the provision of water and electricity supplies. All this work was undertaken by students under the guidance of experienced staff, thereby providing vital practical training in the field. At the same time, detailed geological surveys of surface outcrops and accessible underground workings were undertaken, backed up by diamond drilling, to establish the nature of the mineralisation beneath the Ogofau Pit and to provide a fuller understanding of the complex surface features found in and around this pit.

After 1985 the University continued the development of its own surface infrastructure with the extension of the mine office, the erection of a dual purpose core logging and machine shop, a lamp room, a core shed and finally a visitor display unit describing the mine geology and the use of the Field Centre by various groups of students. Work also continued underground to ensure a safe working environment for both students and visitors. These developments progressed alongside a surface diamond drilling programme (Figure 1.4) designed to determine the true nature of the lode zone and the genesis of the contained gold mineralisation. Time and financial constraints limited progress to one hole per year to depths of up to 140 metres below surface. This drilling was undertaken by undergraduate and postgraduate students under the supervision of experienced diamond drillers. Though drilling was largely concentrated in the Ogofau pit and immediately beneath the Roman Adits (see Chapter 3) some underground drilling was also undertaken in Long Adit (Figure 1.5). Much of this work was funded via the sale of early editions of this booklet and by donations/grants from mining companies and the University of Wales. It gave students invaluable experience in practical aspects of work in a mining operation. A more detailed review of all the work undertaken at Dolaucothi has recently been published (see Isaac 2012 in the selected references at the end of the volume).

Figure 1.4: Diamond drilling at Dolaucothi (P.J. Brabham).

Figure 1.5: Underground drilling in Long Adit, 2000 (P.J. Brabham).

Since 1991 a number of other geological research projects have been carried out in the area immediately surrounding the mine. For example, between 1991 and 1994, a programme of vibrocorer drilling (19 holes), seismic refraction and electrical imaging surveys were carried out to determine the nature and thickness of glacial and post glacial sediments within the Cothi valley to assess the potential for placer gold deposits. Figure 1.6 shows that a significant layer of river terrace gravels does exist overlying glacial clays which could host such gold deposits.

Another important exercise recently undertaken has been the construction of an archive of soil geochemical data based on approximately 1,400 samples collected over various periods since 1979. This information, which included sample locations, was transferred into a computerised geographical information systems (GIS) database thus allowing the production of geochemical contour maps. The analytical data (based on XRF analyses) was validated by resampling previous sites, including those on Allt Cwmhenog, and analysis by modern, more precise, ICP-OES techniques.

The high levels of arsenic in the gold ores have resulted in the release of this deleterious element into the soils along the ridge between Allt Ogofau and Allt Cwmhenog and also into the Cothi valley by natural weathering and the different phases of mining activity. Soil chemical analysis techniques have thus been used by students following an MSc course in Applied Environmental Geology at Cardiff University to assess the degree of contamination of this land based on the accepted limits of 32ppm arsenic for residential use. The results of this work can be seen in Chapter 3 (Figure 3.5). A large area of contaminated land has been defined with a particularly severe problem existing in, and around, the 1938 tailings dam.

Modern GIS techniques such as digital air imagery, LIDAR and 3D terrain modelling have also been used to create a 3D virtual landscape model of the Dolaucothi mine area; some of the results of this are presented in this book.

The 1938 mine tailings dam has also been studied in detail to confirm the historical production figures and to determine the likely recovery of gold in the plant through the losses to the tailings. A 3D map of the dams has been produced; geophysical techniques have provided images of the

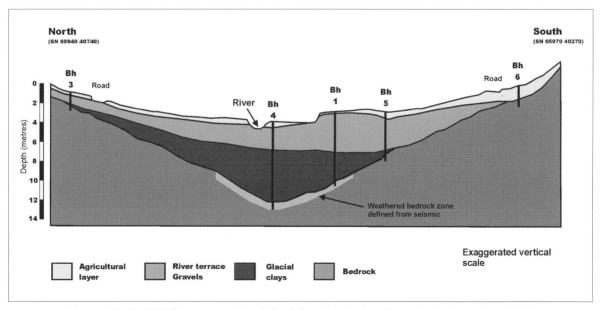

Figure 1.6: Cothi Valley cross-section defined from borehole and geophysical surveying, 1994
(P.J. Brabham, Cardiff University).

dam sediments; vibrocorer drilling of the tailings sediments has determined their thickness and their arsenic, iron and gold contents.

The Dolaucothi Field Centre was also used by a wide range of institutions both from the UK and Europe and the courses taught there were widened from mining-specific to those related to civil engineering, surveying, exploration geophysics and geochemistry, environmental science and engineering geology. After the closure of the Department of Mineral Exploitation in 1989, the Field Centre continued to operate but now under a Management Committee drawn from the School of Engineering and the Department of Earth Sciences at Cardiff University. In 1999, the University relinquished its lease back to the National Trust but continued to use the mine for student field trips but on a less frequent basis.

During the 1980s, a new development at the gold mines was the increasing liaison between the National Trust and the University of Wales in the provision of guided tours of the workings. This began in 1981, with an initial one-month pilot scheme run jointly by the Trust and the Department of Mineral Exploitation, which concentrated, in the main, on the underground workings. In view of its success, a more extensive three-month access scheme was introduced in 1982 with an additional archaeological element provided by the Archaeology Unit at Lampeter. This expanded access scheme continued in succeeding years providing an important local tourist attraction during the summer months.

Alongside this project, there was a steadily growing realisation of the broader educational potential of the gold mines, a point reinforced by a feasibility study commissioned by the National Trust in 1984. This resulted in the decision to improve the tourist facilities at the site by the construction of a visitor centre at the main focus of the workings and by the creation of a tourist trail with appropriate information panels. These facilities became fully operational during the summer of 1986. Since then, the National Trust gradually increased its involvement in tourism at the site and further developed its own visitor facilities to include a shop and café. In 1988, following the closure of the Olwyn Goch lead-zinc mine at Halkyn in north Wales, almost the entire surface installations and associated equipment were moved and re-erected at Dolaucothi thus providing a more realistic mining environment for the visitor. The site thus boasts a headframe, re-established over the old 1930s shaft, and a fully operational winder house, a compressor house with three large 1930s vintage compressors (Belliss and Morcom), a machine shop with an electric locomotive and an Eimco rocker-shovel, a lamp room and a rail system linking the various buildings and the mine workings. Figure 1.7 shows some of these buildings around the new headframe.

The previous editions of this book described primarily the geology, archaeology and mining history of the gold mines at Dolaucothi. However, there was little other reading material of general interest to visitors. University staff felt that visitors, particularly children and their teachers could be helped by the development of educational materials that dealt with the folklore of the area and the Roman period of mining, both subject areas of the National Curriculum for schools in Wales.

Informal discussions in 1988, involving the University, the National Trust and Gwent College of Higher Education, resulted in an initiative aimed at the development at primary school level, of the education potential of the gold mines and the surrounding area. The research programme established at five case-study schools, three in Dyfed and two in Gwent, saw the production of teachers' resource materials and children's worksheets, entitled *Welsh Legend and Culture and The Romans* (see Isaac 1991 and Howell 1991 respectively in the selected references at the end of the volume).

Figure 1.7: The Halkyn headframe and mine buildings at Dolaucothi (B.C. Burnham).

Two events held to mark the success of the Dolaucothi Education project, entitled Education Awareness Day in 1990, and the Official Launch in 1991, were attended by many of the children involved in the case studies and a large number of adult guests and visitors (Figure 1.8). To a great extent, the education initiative could be regarded as heralding the appreciation and excitement of the site and its industrial conservation by a much wider audience than originally anticipated.

Public interest in the Dolaucothi Gold Mines has been further stimulated by National Trust initiatives since taking up the lease in year 2000. Organised visits by schools and societies, together with an opening season extending from March to October, ensure a steady flow of visitors and income. A number of new visitor routes on the surface and in the mine, the development of the gold panning activity, and a range of activity days all point to a future that should allow further development of the site and its exciting potential. Indeed, as this volume goes to press in 2013, work is in progress to revamp the tourist experience with a new on-site trail and information points as part of a wider initiative to present the story of the Roman presence in south-west Wales. The information given in the following chapters will complement this by furnishing an updated description of the geology and mineralogy of the deposit and details as to how it was mined, potentially from pre-Roman and Roman times to the 20th century. Hopefully, this will provide a firm basis for a better understanding of the site by the visitor.

Figure 1.8: A school group engaged in learning at the mines (A.K. Isaac).

CHAPTER 2

LOCATION OF THE MINE WORKINGS

The various mine workings along the north-western flanks of Allt Ogofau and Allt Cwmhenog have been subdivided, for the purpose of description here, into five groups. These workings in their entirety constitute the Dolaucothi Gold mines and their location is shown in Figure 2.1.

Allt Cwmhenog Workings (Figure 2.1, Area 1)

A cluster of old workings lie within the coniferous forest at the north-eastern extremity of the lode zone. They comprise two coalescing pits, the lower one cutting into the base of the upper and containing a deep slot, from which a quartz vein has been selectively mined, as well as two small adits. Around the rim of the upper pit are a series of tanks or reservoirs served by the Annell leat.

Ogofau Workings (Areas 2–4 and 8)

These occur at the central section of the lode zone some 200 metres south-west of the Allt Cwmhenog workings and represent the products of several different phases of exploitation. The most important is the main Ogofau Pit (4), being the largest of the known opencasts and also the focus of the 19th- and 20th-century operations (Figure 2.2). Its originally uneven floor has been successively backfilled with debris forming the foundation upon which the 1930s mine buildings were erected. Today, these are represented by little more than concrete platforms, including the massive base of the compressor house (Figure 5.16). Many of these platforms are now obscured by the new buildings erected on site since 1987. Close to the western end of the pit lies the shaft collar of New Shaft which afforded access to the deeper levels of the 1930s mine and over which the Halkyn headframe has now been established.

Associated with the main pit are three smaller pits known as Mitchell Pit (2), the Roman Pit (3) and Davies Cutting (8). This latter cutting occurs in the rear wall of the Ogofau Pit and is a conical depression, which may have resulted from the collapse of an old underground stope. It is surrounded by cave-like workings of the 19th and early 20th century. An ore-pass set in its base carried material from these old workings into Mill Adit directly below, whence it was trammed out to the mill, which was sited in the south-eastern corner of the Ogofau Pit (Figure 5.4). Beneath a surficial layer of waste rock, this pit is largely infilled with tailings from this plant to a depth of up to 7 metres. On the hillside immediately above the Ogofau Pit is the so-called Roman

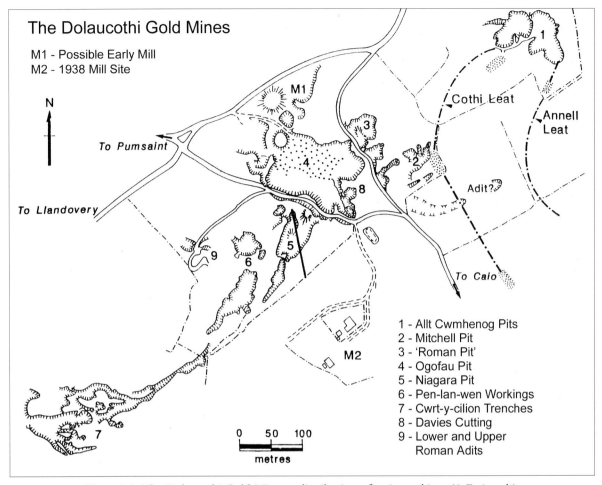

The Dolaucothi Gold Mines

M1 - Possible Early Mill
M2 - 1938 Mill Site

N

To Pumsaint

To Llandovery

Cothi Leat
Annell Leat
Adit?
To Calo

1 - Allt Cwmhenog Pits
2 - Mitchell Pit
3 - 'Roman Pit'
4 - Ogofau Pit
5 - Niagara Pit
6 - Pen-lan-wen Workings
7 - Cwrt-y-cilion Trenches
8 - Davies Cutting
9 - Lower and Upper
     Roman Adits

0   50   100
metres

Figure 2.1: The Dolaucothi Gold Mines – distribution of main workings (A.E. Annels).

Figure 2.2: Detail of the main Ogofau Pit looking north-east from the modern road
which runs along its southern edge (B.C. Burnham).

Pit (3) where pyritic shales appear to have been worked. This pit has been partially infilled with waste rock from the immediately adjacent Mitchell Adit, probably during the 1880 to 1910 period of mining. Higher up the hillside again, and somewhat more isolated, is the Mitchell Pit (2), another rock-cut opencast from which the miners selectively worked a series of quartz veins (Figure 4.2). The age of this pit is uncertain but is thought to be of Roman origin; the Cothi leat, and one of its tanks, lie above its back wall.

The main adit levels driven into the walls of the Ogofau Pit, or into the hillside above, are referred to as Mill Adit, Long Adit, Middle Adit and Mitchell Adit (or Ogof Fawr). Stopes from the Mitchell Adit penetrate through to surface in the Mitchell Pit, while an internal vertical shaft connects it to Long Adit below (Figure 5.2).

Within the Ogofau Pit are a series of more recent buildings erected since 1978 by Cardiff University and the National Trust (NT). On entering the pit from the main road the first building on the right is the NT information centre built in 1986, while on the opposite side of the road is the NT shop and café built over the site of a decline down to the 100 foot level in the underground mine. The next building on the northern side of the pit and beneath Middle Adit is now the NT staff room, but was originally the Mine Office for University College, Cardiff (more recently Cardiff University) during the tenure of its mine lease from 1978 to 1999. A little further on at the eastern end of the pit lies a long shed which now acts as an educational facility for the NT but which originally contained a lamp room, core storage area and a core logging shop for Cardiff students. The cluster of buildings in the central portion of the pit, include a compressor house, a machine shop, a winch house and a lamp room. These were originally sited at the Olwyn Goch lead-zinc mine at Halkyn in north Wales and were re-erected on site in 1988 along with the headframe which dominates the site today. All are now part of the NT visitor attraction. More information on the development of site infrastructure can be gained from the sister volume to this book (see Isaac 2012 in the selected references at the end of the volume).

Niagara Workings (Area 5)

These workings, representing a continuation of the main lode zone in a south-westerly direction, are centred around a large opencast now referred to as Niagara Pit, which opens up, to the north, into the main Ogofau Pit. Up its slopes ran the incline which carried the tramway between the 1930s shaft and the mill adjacent to Pen-lan-wen farm. At its southern side there is an adit (Niagara Adit) which penetrates beneath a narrow surface trench centred on an old winze (surface exploration shaft). It is likely that much of this trench represents a collapse into old underground stopes accessed by this adit.

Pen-lan-wen Workings and the Roman Adits (Areas 6 and 9)

These workings comprise a single deep trench and, to the north-west, an almost circular pit with a steep rock face on its south-western side (6). These are surrounded by numerous old dumps and shallow surface workings. The gold mineralisation exploited by the surface trench was also intersected at depth by a series of adits, whose entrances lie lower down the northern flanks of Allt

Ogofau (9). The upper two, known as Lower and Upper Roman Adits (Figures 4.4 and 4.5), are certainly of pre-19th-century date, while the third, Field Adit, at a lower level in the fields beneath, is of indeterminate age and is currently inaccessible. At the end of the Upper Roman Adit lies a stope and a series of entrances, now walled up, originally connecting with further caverns beyond; these latter appear to have collapsed, in part accounting for the over-deepening of the Pen-lan-wen trench at this point.

Cwrt-y-Cilion Trenches (Area 7)

These are a complex network of shallow trenches connected by a narrow gully to the Pen-lan-wen workings to the north-east. Two deeper pits occur in the central portions of these workings and two short trial adits exist at the south-western limits of the area. The disappearance of the lode zone to the south-west is perhaps due to the presence of a transverse fault which has displaced it.

CHAPTER 3

HOW THE GOLD WAS FORMED

WELSH GOLD MINERALISATION

The presence of gold mineralisation in the old Dolaucothi estate, and particularly in the vicinity of the old mine workings at Ogofau, has long attracted the interest of historians, archaeologists and geologists. The latter, in particular, have been puzzled as to why it is there at all. The questions that they have attempted to answer are firstly what caused the gold to be concentrated in these particular rocks, secondly how was it transported through the Earth's crust and finally where did it come from in the first place.

A study of a map of Wales (Figure 3.1) shows that the Dolaucothi Gold Mines are removed from the main, and better known, gold belt around the south-eastern flanks of the Harlech Dome near Dolgellau. They lie 77 kilometres further to the south in central Carmarthenshire in an area which is close to the southern limit of the central Wales lead-zinc field. An interesting geographical fact, though probably irrelevant from the point of view of the genesis of the gold ore, is that the Welsh deposits, in common with the majority of other gold deposits in Britain lie on, or very close to, the line of longitude 4°W.

The host rocks to the gold at Dolaucothi are shales which lie close to the Ordovician-Silurian contact and which are thus dated at approximately 438 million years. The Dolgellau ores are, on the other hand, in older rocks of Middle to Upper Cambrian age, mainly siltstones and shales, which are thus in excess of 520 million years old. These north Wales gold ores have been exploited from numerous mines located on separate fault-controlled veins, or on strike extensions of the same vein. A well-defined vein can thus be recognised at each mine. At Dolaucothi no such dominant vein exists and we have to consider a mineralised zone in which there is a network of thin discontinuous veins and occasional larger pods or lenses of quartz. Also, in the former area there is evidence of both igneous and volcanic activity as is witnessed by the thick lava and tuff accumulations at Rhobell Fawr and Cader Idris. No signs of such rocks have been found at Dolaucothi and it is thus much more difficult to propose a volcanic origin for the gold there. The nearest volcanic centre is located 22 kilometres to the north-east, close to Llanwrtyd Wells.

Though there are major differences in the geological setting of the two main gold areas of Wales, there are some features which might indicate that they have a common origin and that the process of emplacement was similar. The first of these is the age of emplacement. At Dolgellau the auriferous veins clearly post-date intrusive sills which are related to early Ordovician volcanism and they were also emplaced in faults formed in the Earth's crust at a late stage in the Caledonide orogeny (mountain-building event) which took place 390 to 410 million years ago and which folded the rocks of Wales into a series of north-east to south-west folds. The impact of this

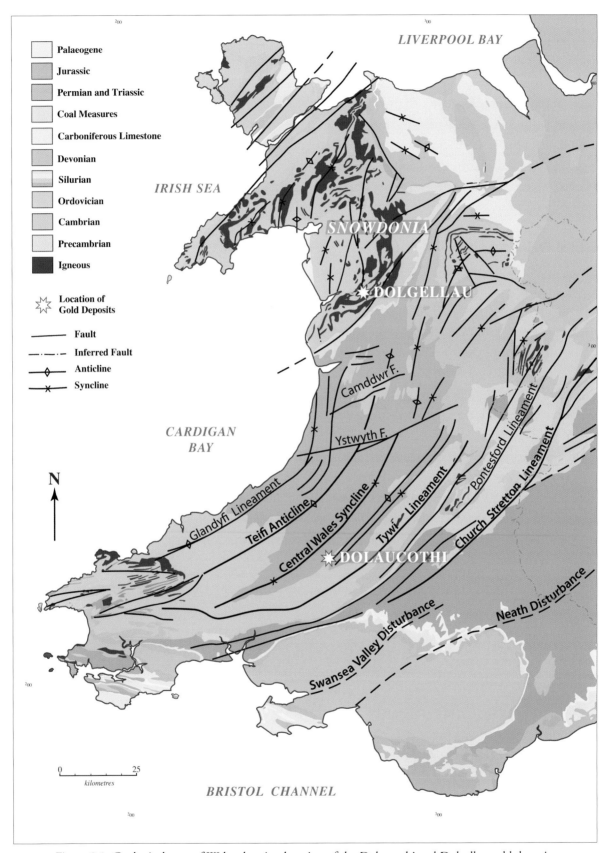

Legend:
- Palaeogene
- Jurassic
- Permian and Triassic
- Coal Measures
- Carboniferous Limestone
- Devonian
- Silurian
- Ordovician
- Cambrian
- Precambrian
- Igneous

Location of Gold Deposits

Fault
Inferred Fault
Anticline
Syncline

LIVERPOOL BAY

IRISH SEA

SNOWDONIA

DOLGELLAU

CARDIGAN BAY

N

Camddwr F.

Ystwyth F.

Glandyfi Lineament

Teifi Anticline

Central Wales Syncline

Tywi Lineament

Pontesford Lineament

Church Stretton Lineament

DOLAUCOTHI

Swansea Valley Disturbance

Neath Disturbance

0   25
kilometres

BRISTOL CHANNEL

Figure 3.1: Geological map of Wales showing location of the Dolaucothi and Dolgellau gold deposits (Courtesy of R.E. Bevans, National Museum of Wales).

mountain-building event can still be seen today in the topographic structure of Wales. At Dolaucothi there is clear evidence that the gold veins were emplaced during, and immediately after, the Caledonide orogeny when the shales were folded, sheared and thrusted by the enormous pressures built up in the crust. The veins were emplaced in, and controlled by, these structures but show clear evidence of deformation, fracturing and other stress-induced features indicating that they do not post-date the orogenetic event. A common age of formation is thus indicated. Secondly, in both areas, the richest ores are to be found where the host rocks contain an abundance of pyrite (FeS_2) as fine disseminated grains or thin concordant or transgressive veinlets. This pyrite predates the gold mineralisation and the presence of the pyritic shales (such as the Clogau Shales in the Dolgellau area) suggests that it played a key role in causing the gold to be precipitated from hot solutions percolating through the fractures.

GEOLOGICAL CONTROL OF THE DOLAUCOTHI GOLD DEPOSITS

Until 1980, when exploration by a Canadian mining company revealed otherwise, gold was considered to be restricted to a small area centred on the old mine workings around the Ogofau Pit. The lode zone has a north-easterly strike parallel to the local Caledonide structural trend and to the local elongation of ridges and valleys. As mentioned above, it also lies within black shales and siltstones of Upper Ordovician to basal Silurian age.

The exploited length of this lode zone is approximately 1.1 kilometres and is marked on the surface by numerous shallow pits, trenches, adits and shafts (Figure 2.1). The lode zone itself follows the axis of a dome-shaped fold structure referred to as the Cothi Anticline, which lies on the north-western flanks of a larger fold, the Towi Anticline (Figures 3.2 and 3.3). This zone also coincides with a belt of intense over-folding and thrusting, approximately 100 metres wide, in which as many as five anticlinal folds are recognizable, either plunging north-east or south-west at between 5° and 20° (Figure 3.4). Recognisable synclinal axes are rare, having been sheared out by thrusting beneath the overturned south-eastern limbs of each of these folds. A concertina-like set of folds and thrusts thus exists which can be recognised over a distance of at least 8 kilometres, though it has locally been displaced by later transverse faults.

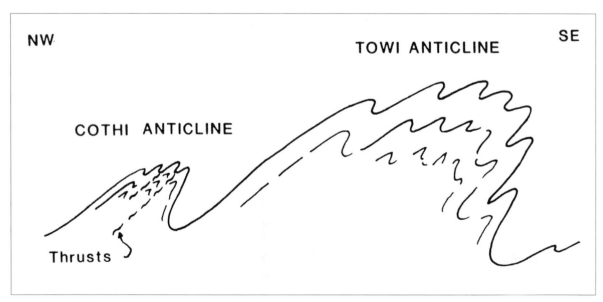

Figure 3.2: Diagrammatic section through the Cothi and Towi Anticlines (A.E. Annels).

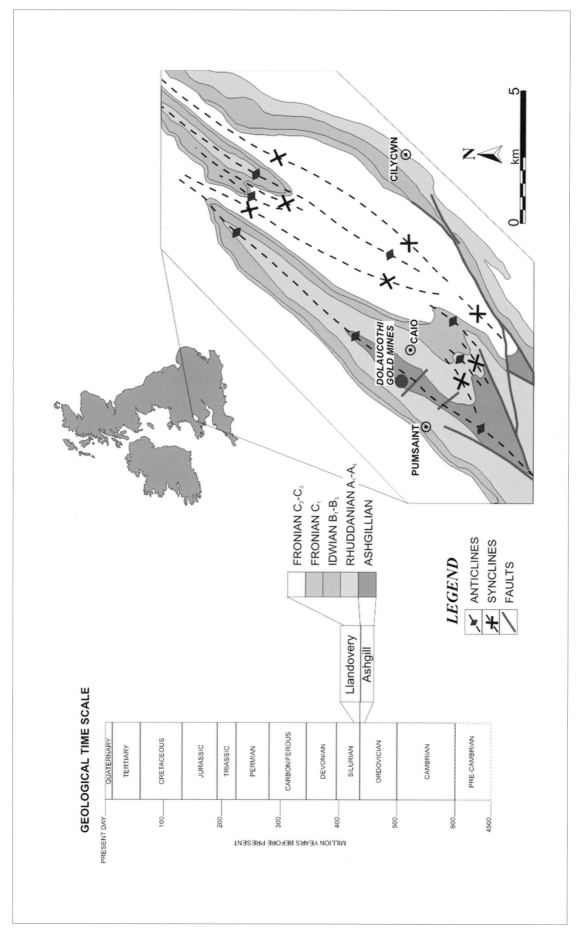

Figure 3.3: Geology of the Cothi Anticline (Courtesy of J. Arthur).

Figure 3.4: Anticlinal fold at entrance to Middle Adit (P.J. Brabham).

Geochemical exploration over the period 1979 to 1983 covered much of the Cothi Anticline and involved the sampling of soils, bedrock and the twigs of trees. This revealed the presence of above background (>25ppm) levels of arsenic in soils along the axis of this fold structure. Arsenic is the main pathfinder element for gold in this part of Wales and reflects the close relationship between this metal and the iron sulphide mineral, arsenopyrite (see below).

Figure 3.5 shows a strong arsenic anomaly centred on the saddle between Allt Cwmhenog and Allt Ogofau and more specifically on the Ogofau Pit. However, the current geochemical dispersion is heavily influenced by the plume of contamination produced by ground- and surface-water transport of arsenic towards the river Cothi and by the spread of mine waste and tailings into this valley. Some of this hydromorphic dispersion is related to natural rainwater drainage and some to contaminated water from old processing operations and from the tailings produced by these plants. The most intense anomaly (purple area on map in Figure 3.5) directly relates to the 1938 tailings dam. An additional source of contamination could possibly relate to early ground-sluicing operations (see Chapter 4) and to the washing of crushed ore to recover the contained gold. Of interest here is the anomaly on the flanks of Allt Cwmhenog immediately north of the Ogofau Pit which extends out into the Cothi valley as a separate plume. This is evidently related to the Allt Cwmhenog Pit and associated leats and tanks and not to more recent mining operations; it too may reflect early ground-sluicing. The age of the small exploratory adits in this pit is not certain and drainage from these could have contributed to this contamination.

Two small anomalies, containing values in excess of 1,000ppm, along the crest of the ridge north-east of the Ogofau Pit, are most likely to be secondary dispersions produced by the weathering and oxidation of outcropping sulphide minerals. The Canadian exploration company, Anglo-Canadian Exploration Ltd., tested the most northerly of these (350 metres to the north of the pit) by diamond drilling (Figure 3.5). This revealed the existence of low-grade gold mineralisation associated with pyrite and arsenopyrite on the strike continuation of the gold-bearing structure in this pit. Unfortunately the thicknesses intersected were insufficient to warrant further exploration at the time. However, this work did extend the total length of the auriferous zone to 1.25 kilometres. This is still only a small proportion of the total length of the tectonised zone which has been recognised along the axis of the Cothi Anticline and which is the major controlling factor for the localisation of the gold mineralisation. The fact that the gold is concentrated over a short section at the centre of this zone implies that other factors have played a role in its localisation, perhaps a transverse late-stage fold and/or fault system.

Diamond drilling continued sporadically after 1985 supervised by geological staff and students from Cardiff University eventually terminating in 1999 when the university withdrew from the site. Most of the drilling up to 1995 was concentrated within or close to the Ogofau Pit and in the fields on the north-western flanks of Allt Ogofau beneath the Niagara Pit. This highlighted the complex structural environment of the gold mineralisation but did confirm the depth continuity of gold mineralisation at levels below the base of the 1930s workings from the main shaft. After 1995 drilling was concentrated directly beneath the Roman adits with the rig positioned immediately outside Lower Roman Adit. Figure 3.6 shows an interpretative section based on the results of this drilling from which it can be seen that the intensity of folding in the two adits and in the drill holes increases towards the stoped areas from broad open folds to tight isoclinal folds over a 60-metre wide interval. The structural complexity is further increased by the presence of numerous shear zones separating sequences that are alternately inverted or 'right-way-

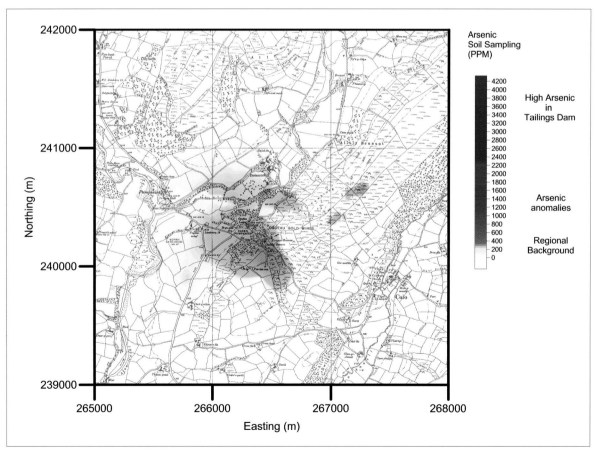

Figure 3.5: Arsenic concentrations in soils around the Dolaucothi gold mines
(Ogofau Pit) (P.J. Brabham, Cardiff University).

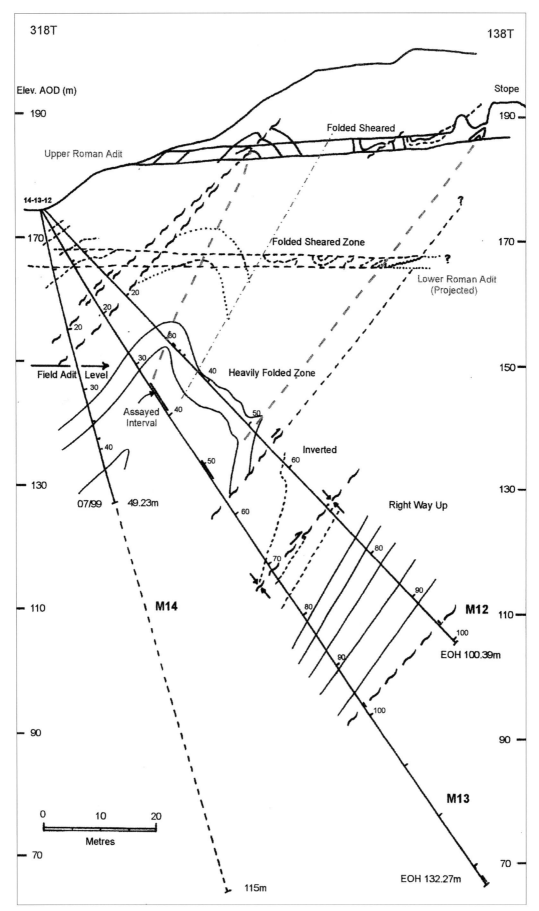

Figure 3.6: Interpretative section of Roman Adits showing drill hole traces (A.E. Annels).

up'. The main mineralised zone is located in the core of the main fold structure in drill hole M13 and could well have been accessed by Field Adit. Unfortunately, the entrance to this adit has collapsed so that direct inspection is no longer possible.

Detailed logging of diamond drill cores in conjunction with the results of previous detailed surface and underground geological mapping, has revealed that the presence of gold at Dolaucothi is directly related to the development of a series of pyritised units within the shales, up to 1.5 metres thick, which are overlain by more competent units of interbedded shales and siltstones. To the north-east and south-west of the mine workings these pyritic units tend to decrease in thickness so that they rarely exceed 10 centimetres, a trend which accompanies the diminution of gold grades in these directions. These pyritic shales were once thought to be the product of hot spring activity on the sea bed but they are now considered to be the result of replacement of receptive horizons by hot hydrothermal fluids rich in iron and sulphur which immediately preceded the influx of gold-bearing, arsenic-rich fluids and the emplacement of quartz-carbonate veins. This hydrothermal activity is also reflected by the presence of chlorite and hydro-muscovite concentrations, veneers and veinlets in these pyritic horizons.

Where the pyritic shales occur within the cores of isoclinal anticlines (Figure 3.7) they have been invaded by arsenopyrite (FeAsS) mineralisation (Figure 3.8) and in the process enriched in gold. This enrichment is particularly pronounced adjacent to an important high angle thrust, or reverse fault, which can be traced through the surface workings in a north-easterly direction. The shear zones associated with such faults have been intruded by a network of thin, discontinuous and irregular quartz-carbonate veinlets or more massive quartz pods (Figures 3.9 and 3.10) and the shales impregnated by pyrite and arsenopyrite. Gold concentrations are patchily developed in both these locations and have been selectively mined at various periods leaving behind large cavernous adits (e.g. Middle Adit – Figure 3.4) and deep trenches (e.g. Niagara, Pen-lan-wen and Cwrt-y-Cilion – Figure 2.1).

Most of the mining activity during the last period of exploitation from 1935 to 1938 was centred on a third type of mineralisation contained within an apparently conformable body of quartz referred to as a saddle-reef and named the 'Roman Lode' by the miners (Figure 5.9). This reef has a strike length of 250 metres, reaches thicknesses of 6 metres on its nose which plunges south-westwards at approximately 28° beneath the nearby Cothi valley to a vertical depth of at least 150 metres. This seems to be a fairly unique feature for the area and appears to be related to a transverse structure that has resulted in a localised reversal of the regional north-easterly plunge of the fold axes. It is probable that this reef was injected into one of the pyritic shale units described earlier as similar material has been recorded along its contacts or as ruptured blocks trapped within the main body of the quartz reef (Figure 3.7). However, there remains the possibility that some of this material is purely an impregnation of the adjacent shales during emplacement of the main vein. This source of ore was exploited from the vertical shaft described later in Chapter 5.

The fourth source of gold ore in the area was a series of planar veins, 0.3 to 1.0 metre wide, which penetrate down into the footwall rocks from the Roman Lode and which were referred to as 'Arsenical Quartz Leaders' by the old miners. These veins were worked over limited dip and strike lengths by means of adits in the hillside above the Ogofau Pit (e.g. Mitchell). Rich concentrations of sulphides were locally present in these veins but only small tonnages of economic grade material were extracted from individual veins.

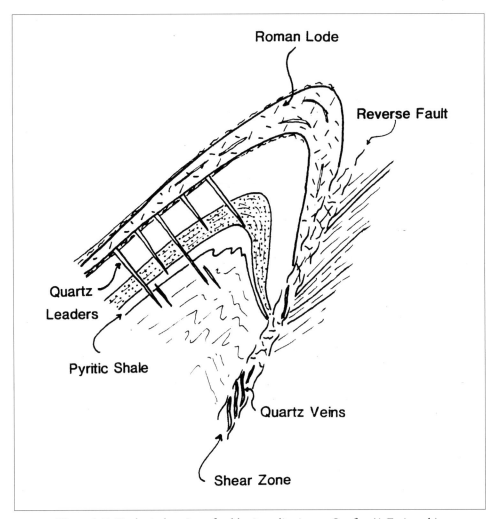

Figure 3.7: Geological setting of gold mineralisation at Ogofau (A.E. Annels).

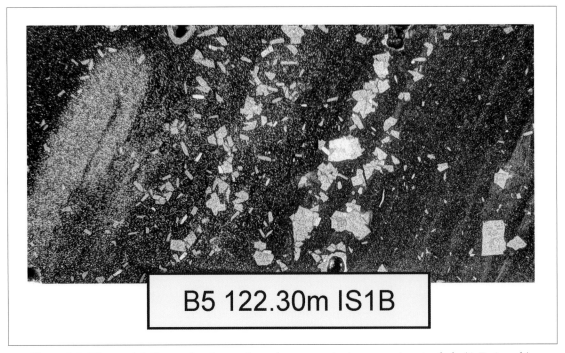

Figure 3.8: Diamond drill core showing pyrite and arsenopyrite impregnations in shale (A.E. Annels).

Figure 3.9: Rich gold veins in Mitchell Adit (P.J. Brabham).

Figure 3.10: Shear zone in Long Adit containing pods and veinlets of quartz (P.J. Brabham).

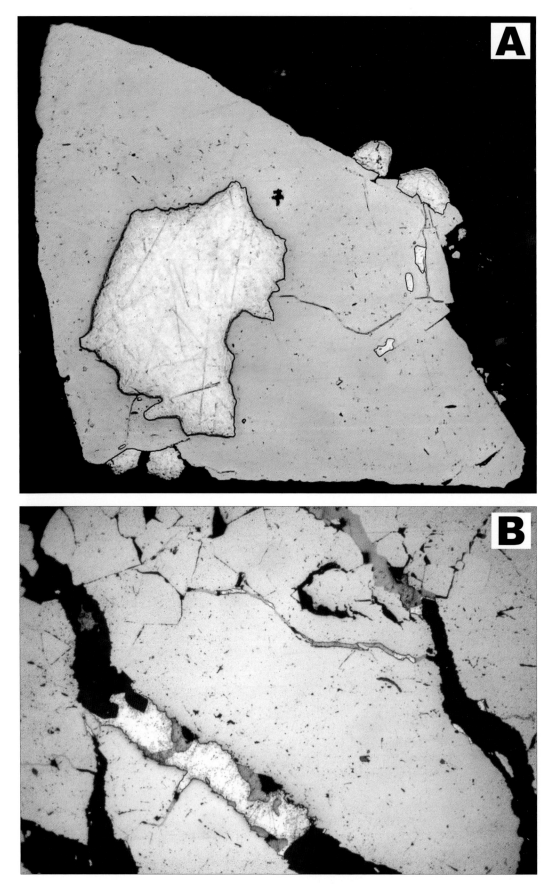

Figure 3.11: Gold seen under the microscope: A) grains enclosed in arsenopyrite with attachments on the margins; B) fracture controlled intergrowths with sphalerite and chalcopyrite (host is arsenopyrite containing crystals of pyrite) (Cardiff University).

MINERALOGY

The sulphides associated with the gold consist of a relatively simple assemblage of pyrite (FeS_2), arsenopyrite (FeAsS), galena (PbS), sphalerite (ZnFeS) and chalcopyrite ($CuFeS_2$) but in varying proportions. Non-sulphide or gangue minerals recorded are quartz, calcite, ankerite, siderite, illite and chlorite. The iron sulphides are far and away the most important minerals present and may constitute up to 25% of the quartz ore or up to 80% of the associated shale. Pyrite occurs as tiny, disseminated, perfectly formed, crystals or as clusters of very fine grains (framboids) or as large crystals in quartz-carbonate veinlets, or as large grains intergrown with, or replaced by, arsenopyrite.

The arsenopyrite itself occurs as beautifully formed diamond, wedge or lath shaped crystals, 1 to 20 millimetres in diameter, which have developed *in situ* in the rock at the expense of earlier sulphides or rock-forming minerals. They thus frequently enclose tiny crystals of pyrite. Large aggregates of arsenopyrite may also occur which enclose ragged, partially replaced grains of pyrite. Though both sulphides occur in quartz veins, only in the thinner veinlets do they display good crystal form. In the coarser-grained, more massive veins, they occur as large irregular aggregates.

The majority of the gold grains in the ores are referred to as 'sulphide locked' in that they occur as inclusions in the iron sulphides, or along fractures in them, or as intergrowths with the base metals in micro-fractures. Some, however, do occur as minute attachments to the outer margins of the iron sulphides but only rarely are these grains visible as most are microscopic at between 15 and 30 microns (Figure 3.11). It is evident that most of the gold has been exsolved from arsenopyrite during cooling of this mineral and then further remobilised by heating during a metamorphic event which followed a period of grain fracturing.

The base metal sulphides of copper, lead and zinc are only rarely found on their own as discrete grains and then they are usually associated with late stage veins some of which contain the iron-rich carbonate, siderite. There is a tendency for lead to be concentrated in the arsenic-rich gold ores while copper and zinc concentrations in the adjacent rocks produce a weak halo of these metals around the gold ores (detectable in soils and the twigs of trees). Most of the base metal sulphides are in fact found as exsolution blebs in the iron sulphides or as infillings of micro-fractures in these sulphides where they are intimately intergrown.

The drilling in the Ogofau Pit has confirmed the existence of a north-south fault crossing the central portion of this pit (Figure 2.1). This was exposed by mining underground and named 'The Lead Lode' (Figure 3.12). This is a late stage structure and is mineralised with the lead sulphide, galena. However, this drilling also detected another fault, this time almost solely mineralised with the zinc sulphide, sphalerite. Both are considered to have been formed during a late stage event along with the more significant deposits of mid-Wales.

ORIGIN OF THE GOLD

During Ordovician times, over the period 519 to 438 million years ago, central Wales was covered by a pile of shales and siltstones, 2 to 2.5 kilometres thick, containing the products of at least three periods of volcanic activity. The last of these volcanic episodes took place 467 million years ago and resulted in the accumulation of lavas and other volcanic rocks in the Llanwrtyd Wells area. Towards the end of the Ordovician, volcanic activity declined rapidly and there were a series of earth movements that resulted in the production of deep-seated faults in the crust or reactivation of older faults, e.g. the Church Stretton Fault along the eastern boundary of the depositional basin.

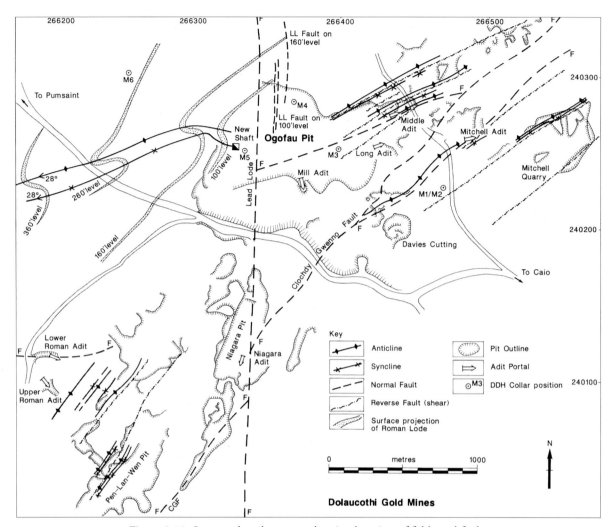

Figure 3.12: Structural geology map showing location of folds and faults
(including the 'Lead Lode') (A.E. Annels).

During Silurian times thick accumulations of black mudstones and siltstones were formed so that by the time that the Caledonide orogeny began, 410 million years ago, the rocks which were to become the hosts to the gold mineralisation, had been buried to depths of 5 to 6 kilometres.

Because of the great depth of burial and abnormally high heat flow, partially related to the previous volcanic activity and partly as a result of the onset of a period of mountain building, the volcanic rocks at the base of the Ordovician and, indeed those beneath in the underlying Cambrian and Pre-Cambrian basement, were subjected to temperatures in excess of 400°C. This caused the rocks to become altered to 'greenschists', so called because of the development of green-coloured alteration minerals such as chlorite, actinolite and epidote. These basal Ordovician and older rocks are not exposed in the Dolaucothi area but where they are, elsewhere in Wales, they show evidence of strong but localised 'greenschist' alteration. Hot waters circulating at high pressures through these rocks are believed to have become enriched in silica and also to have leached various metals from the rocks, particularly the basaltic lavas and tuffs, and in the process to have become enriched in gold, arsenic, iron and other base metals.

The onset of tectonic deformation in Caledonide times thus tapped these fluids and allowed them to rise through fractures (and reactivated older faults in the basement) until they were impeded by structural or lithological traps and cooled sufficiently to allow the replacement of the host rocks by iron sulphides and the precipitation of silica, carbonate and gold-bearing sulphides. This theory thus explains the association of the Dolaucothi gold ores with fracture zones, folded rocks and apparently bedded pyrite deposits. Detailed studies of fluid inclusions in the minerals in the veins, or in the shale impregnations, have indicated that the gold ores have formed at temperatures of between 318 and 372°C.

As mentioned above, most of the gold is associated with the iron-arsenic sulphide, arsenopyrite, and it is believed that initially the gold was trapped in this mineral as it formed but that later, after cooling and grain rupture, the gold exsolved, i.e. it came out of the mineral and concentrated into larger grains along internal fractures. A more detailed description of the geology and genesis of the gold ores has been published (see Annels & Roberts 1989 in the selected references at the end of the volume).

CHAPTER 4

EARLY MINING OPERATIONS

In the absence of documentary sources, our understanding of the earliest phases of mining and settlement is almost entirely dependent upon the interpretation of the surviving archaeological evidence. This is no easy task, as due allowance has to be made for the alterations wrought by the later 19th- and 20th-century operations (though here a careful inspection of Gardner Wilkinson's 1868 survey should provide valuable insights into the pre-modern mining landscape). While most of the academic and popular literature continues to assign the bulk of the visible early exploitation to the Roman period, this hypothesis is by no means unchallenged, in part because of the paucity of dating evidence from the workings themselves (excluding the fort and its related settlements) and in part because the basic mining techniques represented at the site are not absolutely diagnostic of any period between the pre-Roman, Roman and early modern times. The following account is divided into two sections: (i) a brief description of the principal archaeological evidence; (ii) a commentary on the historical development of the mines and the mining methods involved.

THE PRINCIPAL ARCHAEOLOGICAL EVIDENCE

This is best described under three headings: (a) the mine workings; (b) the leat systems and related reservoirs; (c) the ancillary processing and settlement areas.

(a) Mine workings

These comprise a palimpsest of surface and underground features, focused on a saddle now occupied by the main Ogofau Pit (Figure 4.1, Area 4), and on the slopes of Allt Cwmhenog to the north-east and Allt Ogofau to the south-west. The most prominent are the large opencast pits and trenches (Areas 1 to 7), which attest to the successful exploitation of the ore bodies. They were initially worked by opencast methods, more than likely employing water for hushing, ground-sluicing and processing, and were subsequently extended underground in places. By far the largest is the Ogofau Pit, whose overall dimensions are now somewhat obscured by later mining towards the back of the pit, in the area of Davies Cutting (Area 8), by the mature trees masking its rock-cut back walls and by the debris infilling its base (Figure 2.2); this latter provided a convenient foundation for the buildings associated with both the most recent phases of mining and the modern visitor centre. Today this pit extends over 150 metres east-west by 100 metres north-south and its back wall rises to a maximum height of 24 metres above the existing ground surface, though drilling through the debris has indicated that the infill may be between 5 and 12.5 metres deep in places, above what would originally have been a highly irregular floor.

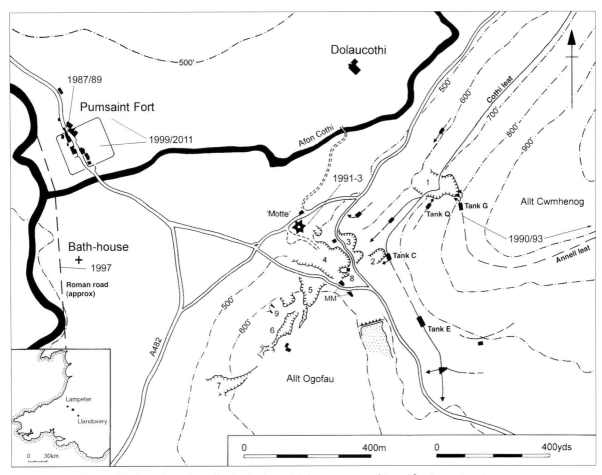

Figure 4.1: Location plan of principal pre-19th-century workings (for Areas 1 to 9 see text.
MM: Melin-y-Milwyr) (After Burnham & Burnham 2004, fig. 1.1, with additions).

Figure 4.2: Mitchell Pit showing slots from which quartz veins have been mined (B.C. Burnham).

Geological considerations suggest that there may have been two deeper areas within this, separated by a barren central ridge; from the westernmost, deeper pit, the workings were pursued underground beneath what is now the modern car-park.

An indication of its original appearance may be gained by reference to two further, if smaller, opencasts, which are located above it on the slopes of Allt Cwmhenog. The first is the Roman Pit (Area 3), even though it too was partly infilled by waste dumping in the 1880s. The other is the more interesting Mitchell Pit (Area 2; Figure 4.2), located higher up the slope immediately below the Cothi leat and one of its associated tanks (C). This certainly preserves much of its original profile, reflecting the way in which early miners had exploited the surface outcrops of two main quartz veins. The existence of several underground entrances, some no longer accessible, indicates that attempts were made to pursue the lode to a greater depth. Such workings were later encountered by more recent underground operations in the 19th and early 20th centuries, as a result of which the original floor of the pit was obscured by waste dumping.

To the north-east, along the line of the Cothi leat and now obscured by a forestry plantation, lies another opencast known as the Allt Cwmhenog Pit (Area 1). Originally it seems to have comprised two coalescing pits, the lower cutting into the base of the upper. Two possible tanks (G and Q) have been postulated on its rim, apparently served by the feeder leats associated with the so-called Annell system. This pit would seem to be one of the earliest of the opencasts, as it is crossed by the line of the later Cothi leat. Similar opencast workings exist on Allt Ogofau to the south-west, which can best be approached from the Pumsaint-Caio road. Besides the main Niagara Pit (Area 5), up which runs the tramway to the 1930s mill, and its smaller neighbour to the west, there are also a series of trenches (Areas 6 and 7) which extend for over half a kilometre as far as Cwrt-y-Cilion Farm, some possibly affected by collapses into underground galleries.

Besides these conspicuous surface workings, there are other less prominent features associated with small-scale exploration and pitting on exposed outcrops. These are often destroyed by later mining activity, but tend to survive in areas of peripheral or unsuccessful exploitation. Numerous examples are known, isolated from the main mining area on both Allt Cwmhenog and Allt Ogofau. Particular interest attaches to one area on the southern slopes of Allt Ogofau, where Lewis and Jones identified several possible circular houses close to a quartz exposure. Within the mine area, extensive surface exploration is visible on the northern slopes of Allt Ogofau, characterised by abandoned spoil dumps bounding hollow scoops and linear gullies. A further area lies on Allt Cwmhenog, between the Mitchell Pit and the forestry plantation, though this may be 19th century in origin.

Early miners also pursued the ore-bearing lodes underground. To them may be attributed several cavernous openings, two of which mark the entrances to the later workings now known as Middle and Mitchell Adits (Figures 3.4 and 4.3). Here they were able to exploit good-grade gold found in association with black pyritic shale and quartz, at points where they had been folded under intense pressure into marked anticlinal structures. More importance, however, attaches to the two adits, now known as Upper and Lower Roman, on the northern slopes of Allt Ogofau (Area 9), and to the extensive galleries or stopes located beneath the Ogofau Pit (Area 4). The two adits, both some 60 metres long, were first described in 1767, though they were not accurately surveyed until 1844. They were both hand-driven, and their walls and roof carefully dressed, as the surviving pick and chisel marks clearly demonstrate. Lower Roman, which is 2–2.5 metres

Figure 4.3: Mitchell Adit showing cavernous entrance (B.C. Burnham).

high, has a very characteristic wedge-shaped profile, which is wider at the top than the bottom (Figure 4.4). Upper Roman, by contrast, is square cut, some 2 metres across (Figure 4.5). Such differences in their profile are not easily explained. Both have usually been interpreted as drainage and haulage passages for a series of underground stopes (only one of which now survives at the end of Upper Roman), though a link with hydraulic mining has also been suggested. Neither can be dated, though a Roman date has been argued on the basis that their size and shape can be paralleled by known Roman tunnels in Spain and Romania.

The galleries or stopes beneath the Ogofau Pit (Figure 5.5), which were discovered during tunnelling in 1935, clearly extended to a depth of up to 44 metres below the current ground surface. Here, early miners had exploited the upper portions of the quartz saddle reef now known as the 'Roman Lode'. Though they are inaccessible today, their Roman date seems assured by the discovery of part of a recognisable Roman drainage wheel which has produced a radiocarbon date of 90±70 BC (Laboratory reference: HAR 2809).

Typologically there is nothing diagnostic about these mine workings to indicate a Roman date, though the drainage wheel fragment must lend some credence at least to the workings in and under the Ogofau Pit, since it is unlikely to have moved far from its original location. A small fragment of probable Roman glass, apparently found 'stratified' in the infill in the Mitchell Pit, is less indicative, as the full details have never been published. No other *in-situ* finds are known from elsewhere in the workings.

Figure 4.4: Lower Roman Adit (Courtesy of the National Trust).

Figure 4.5: Upper Roman Adit (Courtesy of the National Trust).

(b) Leat systems and related reservoirs

The extensive provision and use of water at Dolaucothi has been seen as one of its major features. Work in the late 1960s and early 1970s claimed to have identified at least four separate systems (Figure 4.6), though only one, the Cothi leat, has ever been published in detail. It tapped the river some 11 kilometres upstream and ran on a carefully engineered line with an overall gradient of 1 in 788 to the top of the workings on Allt Cwmhenog, where it served at least two tanks or reservoirs (Figure 4.1, C and E). It can be traced at various points along its route (Figure 4.7). Estimates based on excavation suggest that it was capable of supplying at least 2.5 million gallons daily to the mines.

Of its reservoirs, that at Tank C (Figure 4.8) lies immediately above the rock-cut face of the Mitchell Pit (Area 2) and was arguably linked with its exploitation. It was rock-cut into the hillside at the back, with an outer wall, 8 metres wide, made up of laminated clay and shale with an impermeable clay lining. Excavation has indicated that its outer bank was pierced at one corner by some sort of sluice gate, apparently serving a rock-cut overflow channel, but was later remodelled to supply what has been interpreted as a set of three stepped washing tables used in ore processing. This suggests that the function of this tank had changed during its lifetime. From Tank C, the leat ran on to Tank E (Figure 4.9), the largest on site, measuring some 42 by 10 metres and capable of holding an estimated quarter of a million gallons. Excavation has shown that its outer wall was some 17 metres wide and massively constructed with an inner clay-lined turf core reinforced by a mixed dump of shale, rubble and boulder clay so as to resist the water pressure. Its back wall was cut into the hillside and its rock-cut outflow channel was controlled by a timber sluice-gate. Beyond this, the leat dropped steeply away downhill before serving at least one more tank.

Traces of a second possible leat were discovered in 1969, apparently serving the workings at a higher level than the Cothi leat and extending along the southern flanks of Allt Cwmhenog (Figure 4.10). Only a few isolated sections were actually identified, however, because so much of its course had been affected by afforestation and land improvement, and even these have not been fully published. As reconstructed, it is thought to have tapped a marshy area near the headwaters of the river Annell, some 7 kilometres upstream, before descending to the mines along a relatively steep gradient. Its ultimate destination would seem to have been a pair of tanks (Figure 4.1, G and Q), perched above or alongside the Allt Cwmhenog Pit (Area 1). The importance of Tank G, measuring some 27.5 by 12 metres, lies in the existence of a series of gullies which drop away steeply from its sluice gate and then sub-divide, before plunging into the opencast. These provide the clearest evidence for the use of water in the direct exploitation of the ore bodies, whether by hushing or ground-sluicing.

Some doubts have been expressed about the existence of the Annell leat in the absence of a definitive publication, while the situation in its upper reaches has been complicated by the discovery in 1988 of the Gwenlais leat, apparently extending the system up to 3 kilometres beyond its postulated sources to tap the headwaters of the river Gwenlais. Sections were cut across this in 1990, revealing evidence of a well-defined leat, rock-cut in places (Figure 4.11), with traces of a low bank on the downhill side. While the relationship between these two leats remains uncertain for the present, work on the presumed line of the Annell leat in 1993, in the field immediately south of Tank G, identified the likely traces of its channel and downslope bank.

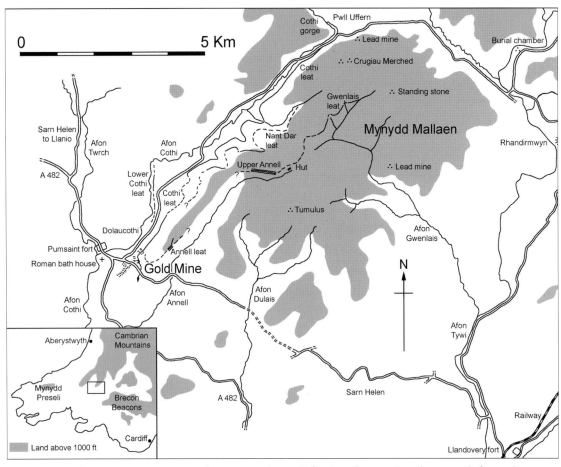

Figure 4.6: Leat systems serving the mine workings (After Burnham & Burnham 2004, fig. 1.2).

Figure 4.7: Detail of Cothi leat above Llwyn-y-Ceiliog Farm (B.C. Burnham).

Figure 4.8: Tank C above Mitchell Pit (B.C. Burnham).

Figure 4.9: Tank E (B.C. Burnham).

Figure 4.10: Detail of Cothi and Annell leats on Allt Cwmhenog (A – Mitchell Pit, B – Tank C, (C – Tank G, D – Annell leat, E – Cothi leat, F – Tank E) (P.J. Brabham).

Figure 4.11: The Gwenlais leat, rock-cut in the foreground; its upstream course is marked by the reed-filled depression (B.C. Burnham).

Two lesser water supplies have also been postulated. The better known of the pair probably tapped the Nant Dâr, a tributary of the river Cothi, and ran on the hillside above the line of the main Cothi leat. While its destination is not known for certain, its relative height and line, if projected, would bring it close to the upper rim of the Allt Cwmhenog Pit. The other supply apparently came off the river Cothi lower downstream than the main Cothi leat; it remains poorly known and its destination has not been determined.

Several isolated tanks, among them I and J, both perched on the edge of the main Ogofau Pit, have been claimed as evidence of exploitation using water power, but their remains are less convincing on the ground and their source of supply unknown. The situation on the Allt Ogofau side of the workings also presents problems. While tanks have been postulated at several points (with varying degrees of confidence), together with a suggestion by G.W. Hall that Upper and Lower Roman Adits might have been connected with hydraulic mining, the precise arrangement by which water could have been supplied from the known systems across the saddle has yet to be established on the ground.

Although leat systems are common on mining sites at many periods, the examples at Dolaucothi have consistently been assigned to the Roman period, based partly on the excavated evidence, partly on analogy with the remains of Roman mining elsewhere, particularly in north-west Spain, and partly because of what seems like an eye-witness account from Pliny the Elder of the large-scale use of water in Spain, most probably in the 70s AD. None of this is absolutely conclusive, though two radiocarbon dates from a peat horizon apparently infilling a section across the upper reaches of the so-called Annell leat (Laboratory references: GRN 16553 and 16720) have been interpreted as indicating that it was three-quarters filled by about 800 AD. Though not without its difficulties, this would have far-reaching implications for our wider understanding of the leat systems as a whole.

(c) Ancillary processing and settlement areas

While considerable fieldwork has been directed at examining the mine workings and the leat systems, the related question of ore processing has not been so thoroughly examined. Several possible sets of stepped washing tables have been suggested, most notably in association with Tank C, apparently comprising a series of rock-cut steps in the local shale (see Chapter 6 for further details on ore processing). It is doubtful, however, whether such washing tables could have coped with the quantity of material produced by the opencasts, which must surely have been more effectively processed downslope from the workings rather than uphill. Some evidence in support of this has been found in places in the fields north of Ogofau Lodge, where quantities of crushed quartz have been recorded during ploughing, while foundation digging at the Lodge itself revealed sedimented beds of crushed material. This area has also produced fragments of several rotary quern-stones and one stone tentatively identified as an axle socket (now all in the Carmarthen Museum).

Potentially more important for our understanding of ore processing was the discovery in 1982, on the sloping ground above the Carreg Pumsaint and the so-called Norman 'motte', north of the main Ogofau Pit (for location, see Figure 4.1), of a series of previously unrecorded earthworks, including a possible header tank and leat (Figure 4.12, Y and Z) and several feeder channels apparently supplying water to a possible wheel pit at the bottom of a sloping ramp. This was tentatively identified as a water-powered crushing and processing mill, an integral feature of

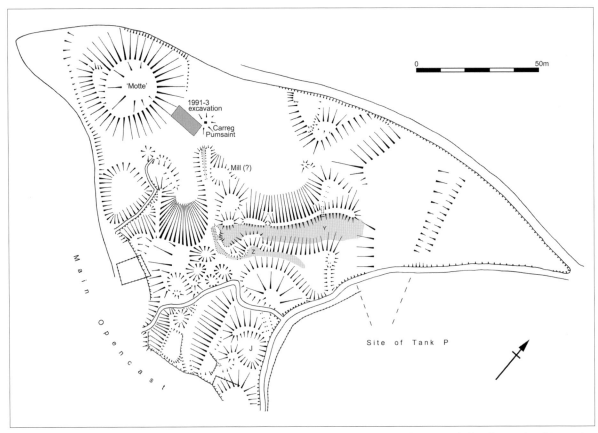

Figure 4.12: Detail of the mill site near Ogofau Lodge (After Burnham & Burnham 2004, fig. 4.1, with additions).

Figure 4.13: The Carreg Pumsaint (B.C. Burnham).

which might have been the nearby Carreg Pumsaint (Figure 4.13). This latter has traditionally been interpreted as a stone upon which ore had been hand-pounded, but more plausibly it finds its closest parallels with the mortar stones associated with the water-driven, trip-hammer stamp mills, best known to us from the pages of Agricola's *De Re Metallica*, written in the 16th century, and from the medieval tin industries of Devon and Cornwall. At the time it was thought to date on technological grounds to the medieval or early modern period, not least because it was not possible to instance a concrete example of the use of any form of water-powered crushing or grinding machinery in the sphere of Roman mining (let alone the type of trip-hammer technology under discussion). This opened up the possibility of a hitherto unrecognised period of mining at Dolaucothi.

In order to explore this complex further, excavation was undertaken between 1991 and 1993 in an area immediately adjacent to the Carreg Pumsaint, where it was thought that related processing wastes might be located sealing the lower levels of the 'motte' and any associated ditch. This revealed a complex sequence of layers, including a succession of thin clay spreads interspersed with intermittent bands of coarsely crushed material (Figures 1.3 and 4.14), all of which would seem to be derived from ore-crushing and related processing in the immediate vicinity. It was also clear that the 'motte' was nothing more than a conical spoil heap. Few finds were made, though they included a fragment of a circular rotary quern. Particular significance thus attached to several charcoal samples sealed in key contexts beneath the processing wastes, the most immediately relevant of which produced a calibrated age range of 43 Cal BC to 331 Cal AD at the 95% confidence level (Laboratory reference: SWAN-37). This clearly suggested a much earlier date than had been expected for the overlying wastes, most probably in the early Roman

Figure 4.14: Processing wastes from the 1991–93 excavations near the Carreg Pumsaint (B.C. Burnham).

period. This raises interesting questions for the date of the postulated mill and about its associated technology, which only further research can clarify. It is enough to note that stones very similar to the Carreg Pumsaint have also been recorded at other undoubted Roman mines in north-west Spain, all of which has encouraged M.J.T. Lewis to argue for a degree of technological development in Roman mining.

As far as 'associated' settlement is concerned, the recorded evidence is almost exclusively Roman. Particular importance obviously attaches to the discovery of an auxiliary fort north of the river Cothi, under the modern village of Pumsaint (Figure 4.15). Excavations here in the 1970s and again in 1989 have shown that it was founded in the 70s AD, following the completion of the conquest of Wales. Its defences were originally constructed of earth and timber, apparently enclosing an estimated area of some 1.9 hectares (4.75 acres). Excavations in the interior have identified traces of its headquarters building, a stone-built granary and sequences of timber structures including both barracks and workshops. As with other forts in Wales, it was subsequently reduced in size sometime in the early 2nd century, when a stone rampart was constructed to enclose a reduced area on the western side (Figure 4.16), estimated at some 0.9 hectares (2.2 acres). This reduced fortlet appears to have been abandoned by the early 120s AD at the latest, though the uppermost levels have been badly damaged by later activity. Geophysical survey in 1999 and again in 2011 has added much to the picture derived from excavation, especially across the eastern side of the fort and the area immediately outside. Of particular interest is the evidence for at least one large, stone-built complex, which is best interpreted as a bath-house, and various other probable timber-built structures aligned on a prominent east-west road.

Roman occupation certainly continued, however, south of the river, in the vicinity of the possible 'bath-house' recorded in the 1830s. Trial excavations in 1997 to the west of its presumed site, together with geophysical survey, explored both the line of the Roman road from Llandovery to Pumsaint and an area of related settlement. Only a small assemblage of finds was recovered, but this indicated a date range from the later 1st to mid-2nd centuries, suggesting that activity here outlasted the fort/fortlet by up to a generation or so. Later activity in and around the mines is far less well attested. One surprise was the discovery during the 1989 excavations at the north end of the fort of the remains of a large, burnt timber building in the base of a vertically sided pit some 2 metres deep (Figure 4.17). Radiocarbon estimates suggest a hitherto unsuspected phase of (military) activity sometime in the 3rd or 4th century. Elsewhere, activity is represented by at least one coin hoard from Erw-Hên, closing with coins of the usurper, Carausius in the later 3rd century, and by a pottery assemblage from the dam of the upper of the two reservoirs straddling the modern road to Caio, now known as Melin-y-Milwyr. This incorporated samian from the 2nd century and coarse-wares extending down to the later 3rd century at least, if not beyond. As yet, none of this can certainly be associated with any *in-situ* settlement.

The possibility of a Norman interest in the mines has often been advanced on the basis of the presence of two possible 'mottes'. That above the workings on Allt Ogofau has long been discounted, while the other at the entrance to the Ogofau Pit cannot now be sustained in view of its reinterpretation as a conical spoil heap. Nothing else is known of the intervening centuries between then and the 17th century, which is represented by a small assemblage of pottery recovered alongside the Roman material from the Melin-y-Milwyr dam. Mention might also be made of some 11 complete pillow mounds of uncertain date, scattered in five groups on Allt Ogofau, which were discovered in 1983.

Figure 4.15: Plan of the Roman fort at Pumsaint as known from excavations
and geophysical survey (After Burnham & Hopewell 2012, fig. 1).

Figure 4.16: The stone wall of the fort at
Pumsaint, 1989 (B.C. Burnham).

Figure 4.17: The burnt timber building inside the fort
at Pumsaint, showing its surviving wall timbers and
plank flooring, 1989 (B.C. Burnham).

HISTORICAL DEVELOPMENT OF THE MINES AND THE MINING METHODS

The starting point in most historical reconstructions of early mining has been the pioneering research of G.D.B. Jones and P.R. Lewis in the later 1960s and early 1970s, augmented by the results of more recent work and ongoing scholarly debate. For Jones and Lewis the single most important phase in the development of the mines occurred in the Roman period, when it was seen as being the only gold mine in Britain and one of the most technically advanced mines in the province. Any pre-Roman mining was thought to have been destroyed by the scale of the Roman operations, with the possible exception of the circular huts which they had identified on the southern slopes of Allt Ogofau, well away from the main focus of the workings. Earlier mining was not considered essential, however, given the well-known Roman propensity for rapid mineral exploitation in newly conquered provinces which, coupled with the fort at Pumsaint, would soon have led either to the discovery of presumed placer deposits in the valley below the main outcrops or to the recognition of the outcrops themselves.

As far as the Roman workings were concerned, Jones and Lewis devised a simple developmental model for the successive phases of Roman exploitation, based on a logical progression from prospecting, through opencast development, to underground stoping, all in close association with a complex system of leats supplying water to the workings. This model drew heavily on the evidence from other sites, most notably Las Medulas in north-west Spain, and on the testimony of Pliny the Elder about the importance of water power in Spanish mining. Much emphasis was initially placed on the use of such water at Dolaucothi in a process known as hushing. This involves the release of a substantial volume of water from a tank or reservoir directly above the working area, a technique which was seen as particularly apposite at the prospection stage and for subsequent debris removal during the early development of the opencasts. Water was also seen as having an important role at the processing stage, when a controlled stream of water would have been used to separate the ore from the waste rock. Such uses were said to account for the different leat systems and for the location and function of the tanks and reservoirs in relation to the majority of the opencasts (most notably Tanks C, G, I and J). A further suggestion that water would have been used in association with fire-setting has now been discredited, as the technique is itself more than effective in dealing with quartz ore bodies which would have fractured easily when heated.

The key to the proposed sequence of development at Dolaucothi lay in the hypothesised relationship between the individual opencasts and the relative sequence provided by the leat systems and their associated features. Especially critical to this was the primacy of the Annell leat and the associated Allt Cwmhenog Pit, apparently guaranteed by the way in which the Cothi leat was subsequently contoured around the latter at a later date. The resulting model can be summarised simply: (i) limited pre-Roman exploitation; (ii) the development of the Annell leat and its tanks (and possibly the Nant Dar?) in connection with the exploitation of the Allt Cwmhenog Pit; (iii) the development of the larger and more efficient Cothi leat and its tanks in connection with the exploitation of the main Ogofau Pit and the other opencast pits on Allt Cwmhenog; (iv) the subsequent exploitation of the underground resources beneath the Ogofau Pit. Quite how this sequence extended to the trench workings and opencasts on Allt Ogofau remains problematical, in the absence of definitive evidence for how water could have been supplied above the workings. The creation of at least two adits on this side, however, is clear evidence for the exploitation of underground resources beneath the surface trenches. Based on this, Jones and Lewis felt confident to argue that the basic form of the mines as we see them today had already taken shape in the Roman period.

In a re-assessment of this sequence, D.G. Bird has argued that the provision of so much water so high above the workings would not have been justified if it had been simply for initial prospection and subsequent debris removal. Instead, he emphasises the extensive similarities between Dolaucothi and the Asturian mines in north-west Spain, where significant quantities of water were apparently employed in a process of more or less continuous ground-sluicing (sometimes loosely referred to as 'hydraulicing' in the literature). His thesis is that, at Dolaucothi, the Romans recognised the presence of extensive areas of relatively soft and weathered pyritic shale containing high quantities of free gold; this echoes a suggestion first made by G.W. Hall in connection with the exploitation of the deposits on Allt Ogofau. Bird maintains that this would have been worked by directing a powerful stream of water onto different parts of the deposit as required, so that the resulting debris could be directed downhill into channels or sluices where the gold could then be recovered. The process was no doubt aided and abetted by workers who would break up the deposits and direct them into the streams. Such activity probably helps to explain the presence of several linear gullies, sometimes referred to as 'outwash channels', which have been identified on the flood-plain below the workings. This method does not preclude the use of hushing either during the initial stages of exploration or subsequently when the workings were further extended to adjacent areas. While such ideas usefully extend the original Jones and Lewis model, they do not significantly alter the developmental framework.

It is highly likely that the early miners concentrated on the extraction of free gold, which would have confined their operations to those areas where surface weathering had been sufficiently extensive to weather the sulphides and so release the fine grains of gold trapped within. The extent and depth of this clearly varied, as the workings themselves demonstrate. Drilling has indicated that, typically, weathering and oxidation occurs to depths of 20 or 30 metres, though locally in heavily fractured ground, greater depths are achieved. This no doubt accounts for the extension underground of the Ogofau Pit to a depth of up to 44 metres below the current surface. It has been calculated that early miners may have removed as much as 500,000 tonnes of rock from the main Ogofau Pit alone; if we make an assumption that one third of this contained gold mineralisation grading 5 grams per tonne, then this would have yielded some 830 kilograms of gold (the equivalent of about 26,000 troy ounces), representing a cube-shaped block with sides of some 36 centimetres in length. This might seem a somewhat meagre return for the effort expended, so either the operation was only made 'profitable' by virtue of the availability of cheap labour, or else the miners were working higher-grade ore than that recorded in more recent operations.

The chronology of this early exploitation is difficult to define with precision as so little excavation has been focused on the workings themselves and very few *in-situ* finds have been recovered. Instead we are largely dependent upon dating material (primarily pottery) drawn from sites which are essentially peripheral to the mines, primarily the fort at Pumsaint, the 'bath-house' and settlement south of the river Cothi, and the upper of the two dams now known as Melin-y-Milwyr. Two further, if less easily quantifiable, factors concern the overall volume of material being extracted and processed and the size of the available workforce.

Extrapolating from the available dating evidence it is possible to argue that there was a major phase of mining at the site, initially under the direct control of the military from soon after the foundation of the nearby fort in the mid-70s AD through to its abandonment by the early 120s AD, following a reduction in size to a fortlet soon after 100 AD. Certainly, the development of the Annell and Cothi leats must imply a considerable level of expertise, which could only have been supplied by army personnel in what was recently pacified territory. More than likely the initial workforce would have comprised local conscripts, condemned criminals and perhaps even some slaves. This initial military phase was probably succeeded by a period of civilian mining, at which time the mines would have been leased out to civilian contractors, in line with what is known to have happened elsewhere in Roman Britain. Their focus of settlement would seem to have lain along the line of the Roman road south of the river Cothi, in the vicinity of the 'bath-house', where operations most probably continued on a diminishing scale for perhaps a further generation or two. Whether mining continued in any form beyond this is impossible to determine at present, as the later material from the Melin-y-Milwyr area cannot be associated with any definite settlement.

Such rapid exploitation accords well with the known Roman practice of developing new provincial resources as quickly as possible, while the subsequent decline in production (and profitability?) probably reflects the increasingly sulphidic nature of the ore body and the opening up of newer and richer resources in the wake of Trajan's conquest of Dacia in the early years of the 2nd century. Despite the dangers of extrapolating from the settlement narrative to the dating of the mining sequence, such evidence as has been obtained from the mine area and the associated leats has consistently lent support to the framework suggested here.

While the Jones and Lewis model has generally stood the test of time, it has not been without its critics in the archaeological and mining literature. One such challenge arose in the wake of an Anglo-French exploration of the site in 2000, led by B. Cauuet, which drew extensively on her experience of later prehistoric hard-rock mines in Limousin. She drew a distinction at Dolaucothi between the primary deposits of hard rock, which could have been effectively exploited by tool-working and fire-setting, and the secondary deposits which could have been worked by hydraulic systems. From this she argued that a large part of the workings could have been exploited in the pre-Roman period, with the Romans arriving in the 70s AD to inherit a site already extensively worked by opencast methods (if not also by underground technology), which they subsequently sought to rework, in part by extending further underground (as the waterwheel fragment attests) and in part by the exploitation of the secondary deposits making use of large-scale hydraulic systems. Much of this remains speculative, in the absence of supportive dating evidence from the workings, though a case for prehistoric mining is strengthened by the evidence now accumulating from elsewhere in Wales and beyond. Equally speculative is a second suggestion made by C.S. Briggs, based in part on his preliminary assessment of the 1868 survey by Gardner Wilkinson, that the workings most probably had a medieval or post-medieval origin and that they were most likely exploiting metals other than gold.

All this emphasises that much still remains to be learnt about Dolaucothi, if we are to prove beyond reasonable doubt the extent (or otherwise) of Roman mining. The time is now surely ripe for targeted excavation within the workings. What followed in the 1870s and beyond is another story.

CHAPTER 5

LATER MINING HISTORY

19TH- AND EARLY 20TH-CENTURY OPERATIONS

The available literature, prior to 1846, makes it clear that visitors to the mines were not aware of the nature of the metal that was being extracted. Sir Joseph Banks for instance, in a journal dated 26th August 1767, describes one such visit to the mine workings at Dolaucothi and, in particular, to the Upper Roman Adit near Pen-lan-wen Farm (Figure 4.5). Though he suggested that the Romans might have been responsible for the adit construction, he obviously had no knowledge of what was being mined. The only record of mining at Dolaucothi during this period is a contract between the Johnes family of the Dolaucothi mansion, dated 27th October 1797, and a William Jones, which was for the sinking of a shaft at 10 shillings a yard for the first two yards and then 12 shillings and 6 pence thereafter. The location of this shaft is unknown and no mention was made of its purpose. At this time this new venture was considered to relate to a lead and copper mine. Even as late as 1839, the renowned geologist, Sir Roderick Murchison, also failed to determine the nature of the metal that had been mined, though he concluded that the workings were Roman in origin.

In 1844, however, Sir Warrington Smyth of the Geological Survey rediscovered gold on the site, and later, Sir Henry de la Beche, another famous geologist, made the first gold assay on quartz from the mine. This attracted three Australians to the site in 1853, who were sufficiently encouraged by their examination of the old workings to erect a water-driven, five-stamp mill for crushing ore. This operation was, however, short-lived.

In 1855 the Cambrian Archaeological Association visited the site and were probably accompanied by Sir John Gardner Wilkinson, an eminent Egyptologist. This clearly kindled his interest in Dolaucothi and South Wales in general because it eventually led to the Johnes family commissioning him to undertake a survey of the mines in 1868. The maps he produced provide a detailed picture of the old workings as they existed prior to later 19th- and 20th-century operations. Clearly shown are numerous drainage channels leading to the river Cothi and also the original shape of the Ogofau Pit prior to its backfilling with waste rock and tailings during these later operations. C.S. Briggs has recently suggested that the campsite marked on Gardner Wilkinson's map could be that occupied by the Australian miners in 1853.

Soon after 1868 the Mining Journal reported activity at Dolaucothi during which a water wheel had been erected on the stream immediately adjacent to an area now known as Davies Cutting, which lies immediately behind the south-east wall of the Ogofau Pit (Figure 4.1, Area 8), presumably named after a Mr. A. Davies who used it to provide power for a crusher (Einion Eur Glawdd as it was called – translated as 'Fairy of the Gold Mine'). A small, heavily silted reservoir can still be seen at this location, together with a second pond with which it is interconnected on the other side of the modern road to Caio, now known as Melin-y-Milwyr.

In 1872, Mr. J. Johnes, the owner of the Dolaucothi estate at the time, is reported to have purchased one or two ounces of gold from two Welshmen recently returned from Australia, who were granted permission to work on the mines. Most of their ore came from quartz veins exposed in old surface and shallow underground workings, but the low grades encountered, caused them to abandon the operation later in that year. Much of this ore was probably obtained from the area now known as Davies Cutting. Examination of the Mineral Statistics in the Annual Reports of HM Inspectors of Mines over the 15 years from 1873 to 1888 confirms that the Dolaucothi Mine was inactive over this period and that the early 1870s workings had ceased prior to 1873.

On 27th December 1887, Lt. General Sir James Hills Johnes KCB requested a lease for the Dolaucothi Mines under the Mines Royal Act so that they could be sublet by the family. In April 1888 the lease was taken up by a Mr. Jones, probably a Mr. Edward Jones, who formed the South Wales Mining Company Ltd. with a nominal capital of £60,000. The annual rent payable was £100 and the initial royalty was set at 1/30th, but this was changed in 1891 to 1/16th. The mine was reopened later that year and in the following year the company leased the former Cambrian Tin Plate Works at Llanelli in order to process any future gold ore production. Mr. Edward Jones and his nephew Capt. Telford Edwards, whom he had appointed as manager, drove an adit into the hillside to the east of the Ogofau Pit which was later to be called Mitchell Adit (Figure 4.3). This adit was an extension of a cavern, originally mined at an earlier date possibly by the Romans, on the upper bench of the Ogofau Pit. A rail track from these workings branched immediately outside the adit; one branch passed via an archway into the so-called Roman Pit (Figure 4.1, Area 3) where waste rock was dumped, while the other crossed the track to a steep chute down which the ore was delivered to the mill beneath. The rear wall of this mill is still visible today (Figure 6.2). Jones also drove most of Long Adit (Figure 5.1), immediately below the mill site, and interconnected the two adits with a winze, some 25 metres deep. Between 5 and 16 men were employed at various times to undertake this work.

Though the 1870s mill had been powered by a water wheel, the 1888 mill was powered by a steam engine. This mill had a capacity of 30 tons per day and contained a stone breaker, Cornish rolls, jigs and a Britten pan. However, though sampling on the Mitchell lodes undertaken in 1890 gave values of 6 to 12 dwt (i.e. 10 to 20 grams per tonne) over widths of 24 to 48 inches, the recovery from the mill feed was only 1.5 dwt (2.5 grams per tonne). Such a small amount of gold was produced at this time that no royalties were in fact paid to the Crown and mining had virtually ceased by early 1893.

Figure 5.1: Long Adit portal (P.J. Brabham).

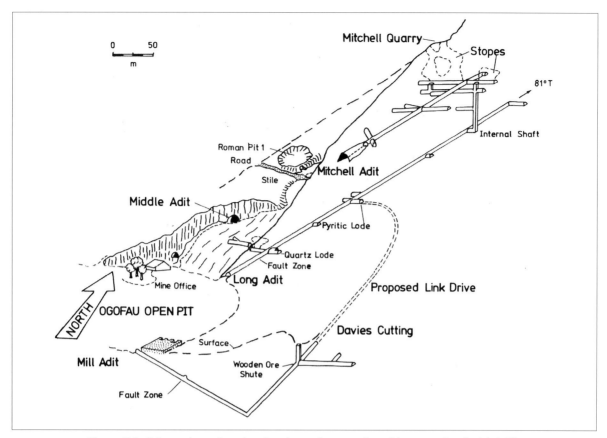

Figure 5.2: Schematic section showing the underground workings associated with Mill,
Mitchell and Long Adits (A.E. Annels).

The annual reports of the Inspector of Mines record that no production was achieved at the mine until 1891 when 100 tons were produced. However this conflicts with the production of only 50 tons, from which nearly 5 ounces of gold were recovered, in the List of Mines for 1891. It is also claimed that 200 tons of ore had been extracted by 1892 when operations ceased. None of this was processed at the Tin Plate Works which had been relinquished by this time and it is thought likely that this ore was treated later by Vivian's Hafod Works in Swansea but no information exists as to gold recovery. The mine site was abandoned in 1893, the lease expired on 4th April 1894 and the plant, which had originally cost £3,000, was sold in September 1894 for £300. The Mining Journal does report some development in 1895, but this was very limited and the Company finally went into liquidation in May 1897.

In 1905, the Johnes family employed Mr. James Mitchell, a Cornishman with experience in South African gold mines, to re-establish mining on the site. He constructed a 5 by 750 lb. stamp mill and used a Wilfley shaking table to concentrate gold. During the year 1905–1906 he extracted 381 tons of ore from the old workings, probably from Mitchell Adit, from which he obtained 44 ounces of gold and 6.6 ounces of silver. This was sufficient to yield a profit of £172.

Encouraged by these results, Mitchell formed his own Company – Ogofau Proprietary Gold Mining Company Ltd. – and during the remainder of 1906 processed 360 tons of ore yielding 28 ounces of gold and 5 ounces of silver, providing a profit of £105. This ore was obtained from continued development of the upper levels leading to a small pit above Mitchell Adit (Figures 4.1, Area 2, 4.3 and 5.2). However, lack of capital prevented simultaneous exploration and extraction of ore reserves and from 1907 to 1909 up to 12 men were engaged primarily on mine development.

Seventy-five tons of ore were processed in 1908, however, yielding 11 ounces of gold. At this time it is almost certain that Mitchell further extended Long Adit. A second adit, whose portal now lies adjacent to the concrete foundations of the 1930s compressor house, was also driven for a distance of 40 metres; this was originally called Davies Adit, but is now known as Mill Adit. This extensive development absorbed all the available capital and the lease was subsequently sold in 1909 to Cothy Mines Ltd., who then employed Mitchell as Mine Manager.

Official statistics provided by the Inspector of Mines for the whole period 1905 to 1908 are at slight variance with the production figures quoted above. A total of 897 tons (911.4 tonnes) were mined yielding 106 ounces (3,297 grams) of gold indicating an average grade of 3.62 grams per tonne.

In 1909 Cothy Mines Ltd. are recorded as producing 23 ounces of gold from 96 tons of ore. This largely came from seven veins in Mitchell Adit, one of which is illustrated in Figure 5.3, and which contained variable amounts of arsenopyrite. One pyrite-rich vein, 75 centimetres wide, assayed 10 dwt gold (17 grams per tonne) and 1.5% arsenic, while another, 60 centimetres thick and containing arsenopyrite, assayed at 12 dwt (20 grams per tonne) and 9% arsenic. A total of 70 tons of ore came from these veins averaging 8 dwt 4 grs (14.3 grams per tonne). The value of this ore at the time was 32s 8d per ton of which 19s was recovered by amalgamation and 12s worth by cyanidation. Presumably the remainder was lost to tailings. The cost of mining and processing at the time was estimated to be 12s a ton. Additional ore was obtained from pyritic shales from Davies Cutting and also from Mill Adit which gave grades as high as 6 dwt 12 grs (11.7 grams per tonne) and 1.5% arsenic. Figure 5.4 shows the mill in 1910 in the south-eastern wall of the Ogofau Pit opposite Long Adit.

On the basis of their experience of mining in and around the older workings centred on the Ogofau Pit, the management realised the potential of the pyritic shales and the associated sulphide-rich veinlets. They had also gained an understanding of the geology of the area and thus advised the Company to sink a shaft at the north-western side of the pit, from which an exploration cross-cut could be driven south-eastwards for a distance of 100 metres to investigate, at depth, the mineralisation most probably exploited by the Romans.

This shaft was duly commenced and sunk to a depth of 29.3 metres by the end of 1909. However, at a depth of 25.3 metres, this shaft intersected a vein, later to be called the Roman Lode, with a north-westerly dip of 40°. This massive quartz vein, 1.2 metres thick, with pyrite, arsenopyrite and minor galena mineralisation, had a concordant habit, with a corrugated hangingwall beneath 7 to 15 centimetres of soft dark clay, and was successively underlain by 30 centimetres of shale with quartz stringers and by 10 centimetres of laminated quartz and pyrite. The latter assayed at 10 dwt (17.1 grams per tonne), while the main vein assayed at 11 dwt 4 grs (19.3 grams per tonne). The existence of such a lode had not been anticipated, because it was covered by at least 10 metres of debris in the base of the pit. Also, its upward extension had been removed by faulting (the Clochdy Gwenno Fault, Figure 3.12).

By February 1910 the south-east cross-cut on the 100 foot level had been driven a distance of 25.3 metres (Figure 5.5), intersecting two zones of pyritic shale and an extensive network of quartz stringers and quartz leaders penetrating down from the quartz reef above. Sampling at the time by B.W. Holman indicated that virtually the whole of this cross-cut was economic, with most assay samples lying between 2 and 20 dwt (3.4 and 34 grams per tonne). Short drives had also been developed in the Roman Lode to expose the hangingwall for a distance of 7.5 metres to

Figure 5.3: Small stope in Mitchell Adit centred on a 'Quartz Leader' vein (P.J. Brabham).

Figure 5.4: Mitchell's mill in 1910 located in the eastern section of the Ogofau Pit (Mining Magazine, May 1911).

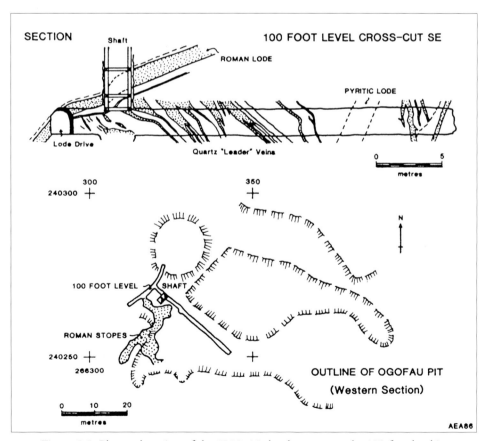

Figure 5.5: Plan and section of the 1909–10 development an the 100 foot level in relation to the Ogofau Pit and the early stopes (A.E. Annels).

the north-east and 9.5 metres to the south-west. The latter was to prove the downfall of the operation, for this face penetrated old workings which flooded the level. The pumps at the time could not cope and the mine had to be abandoned. These old workings are probably Roman stopes which lay to the west of the shaft and which had been worked from the base of the old pit down to depths of 44 metres below the shaft collar.

Mitchell also reworked old tailings to a depth of 4 metres adjacent to a spoil heap (once referred to as a 'motte') at the entrance to the Ogofau Pit; he worked a cross-lode in the Allt Cwmhenog Pit; sank a small trial shaft (3 metres deep) in the centre of the Ogofau Pit and finally sank another shaft a quarter of a mile away at an elevation of approximately 190 metres (50 metres above the main shaft) in order to cut through the successive levels mined by pre-19th-century workers beneath Pen-lan-wen. The possible location of the collar of this shaft lies within a trench above the stopes accessed from Niagara Adit. However, his efforts were in vain, for the company was by now, insolvent. To add to their problems, they were unable to find a smelter which would accept their arsenical sulphide concentrates and their attempts to recover gold by direct amalgamation failed as the ore became less weathered. Official statistics record production for Cothy Mines Ltd. for only two years (1909 and 1910) totalling 96 tons (97.5 tonnes) from which 23 ounces (715 grams) of gold were recovered indicating a grade of 7.33 grams per tonne. During this time 10 to 12 miners were employed underground and 6 to 10 on surface; by 1911, the numbers had dropped to 2 men underground and and 2 on surface. Cothi Mines Ltd. was finally dissolved sometime between 1916 and 1932.

The total recorded production between 1905 and 1910 was thus 933 tons (1,009 tonnes) yielding 129 ounces (4,012 grams) of gold indicating a combined average grade of 3.98 grams per tonne. This is compatible with those achieved in the 1930s discussed later.

MINING IN THE 1930s

The abandonment by Britain in 1931 of the gold standard, by which the price of the metal had been controlled, resulted in the creation of renewed business interest in gold mining. This eventually led to the formation of Roman Deep Ltd. in 1933 to assess the feasibility of working the quartz reef exposed by Mitchell in 1910. This company negotiated a 60-year lease from the owner of the Dolaucothi estate and appointed Mr. Jack Wilson as Mine Manager. Professor Bernard Holman from the Royal School of Mines in London, was retained as consultant. During the first year, Mitchell's shaft was dewatered and a timber headframe built (Figure 5.6). The exposures of the Roman Lode at the 100 foot level, and the underlying heavily veined and pyritised shales, were sampled by another consultant, Mr. Tudor G. Trevor, in August 1933. Though good grades were confirmed in the former, the values of the latter did not meet the expectations aroused by Holman's 1910 sampling. Trevor's report, however, recommended that the results were sufficiently encouraging to warrant the deepening of the shaft to the 300 foot level at a cost of £6 per foot, and the driving of levels at depths of 200 and 300 feet at a cost of £1 10s per foot.

In October 1934 another consulting engineer, Mr. R.C. Wilson, recommended to the then manager of Roman Deep, Mr. Lancelot Owen, that additional capital be raised (£175,000 to £200,000) to allow extension of the shaft to a depth of 500 feet. Early in 1935 a new company, Roman Deep Holdings Ltd., was formed to continue supervision of the mine development with the additional funding. Eighty-six men were engaged at this time on repairing and deepening

Figure 5.6: Wooden headframe erected in 1933 to allow access to Mitchell's 1909 shaft
(Industrial and Maritime Museum, National Museum of Wales).

Mitchell's shaft, henceforth known as New Shaft, and by 1935 up to 900 feet of development had been completed on the 160 foot level. Sampling of the lode so exposed gave values of between 4 and 7 dwt (7 to 12 grams per tonne) over mineable widths. This development thus allowed bulk sampling of the ores for metallurgical testing. It was realised by this time that the ore was not free milling and thus not amenable to direct cyanidation and that production of sulphide concentrates would be necessary by the froth-flotation process referred to in Chapter 6. At a time when the gold price was still only £7 per ounce, it was estimated that the break-even grade for profitable extraction of gold ore would be 3 to 4 dwt (6 grams per tonne).

Evidence that the mine was producing limited amounts of gold at this time is revealed by the fact that Roman Deep Ltd., together with Prince Edward and Marina Mines in the Dolgellau gold belt, provided gold for the wedding ring of HRH, The Princess Marina, Duchess of Kent, in May 1935. This bar of gold has since been used for other royal rings.

By July 1935 the main development on the 160 foot level was complete, as also the access cross-cut from the shaft to the 260 foot drive, together with a small amount of driveage on this level. Also completed was a loop drive on the 160 foot level which was driven in the footwall of the Roman Lode to investigate the ground beneath the Roman workings in the Ogofau Pit. Another cross-cut on the 100 foot level had also been driven beneath this pit. This development can be seen on Figure 5.7.

It was during this redevelopment of the mine in June 1935, that Roman Deep Holdings Ltd. broke into the ancient workings that had earlier been the downfall of Cothy Mines Ltd. These workings, at the end of West Drive on the 100ft level (Figure 5.7), contained the archaeological finds described by O. Davies. This large cavernous stope is described as being 23.5 metres long, 7.9 metres wide and 4.5 to 6.0 metres high. Deeper extensions down towards the 160 foot level

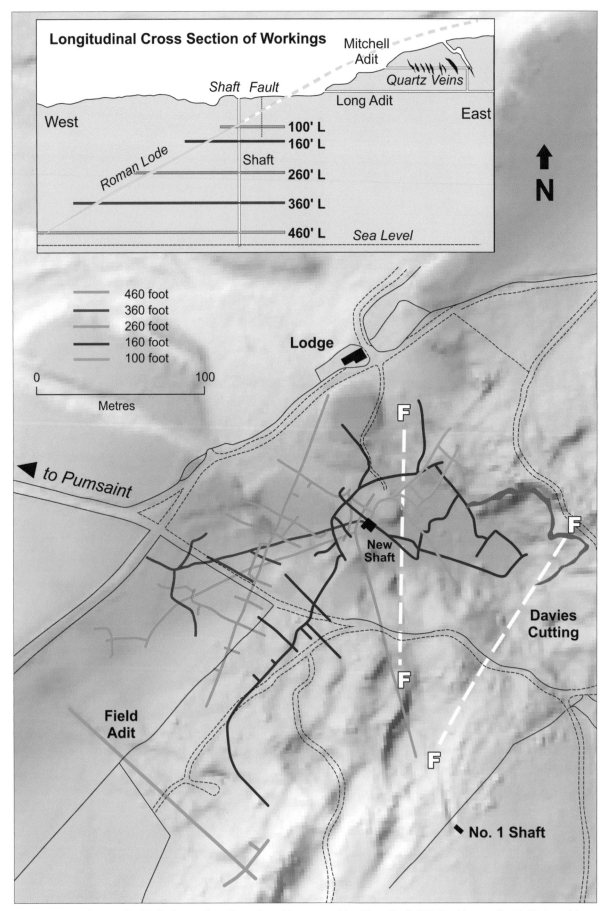

Figure 5.7: Composite level plan and section of workings served by New Shaft (P.J. Brabham, after A.E. Annels).

had an inclination of 50° and thus were almost certainly exploiting Footwall Quartz Leaders similar to those in Mitchell Adit. This area was abandoned by the end of September 1935 as being too dangerous, presumably due to instability in the roof of the stope where the Roman Lode had been undermined by footwall stoping and by dewatering and mining-related vibration at lower levels.

Dr. A. Brammall, in a report to the Manager, Mr. Bryant, dated October 1935, revealed that by this time it had been appreciated that the Roman Lode was a saddle reef, i.e. a quartz vein intruded conformably with the country rock, and that it was controlled by a westerly plunging anticlinal fold and an associated syncline with a total base span of 75 metres. At the crest or troughs of these folds, the reef was thickest and was often barren and vuggy. However, where the saddle reef was in contact with the country rock, both were enriched in sulphides and gold. Along strike, to the north-east and south-west, the reef thins into a complex shear zone with veins and stringers of quartz cutting heavily contorted and sheared shales (Figure 5.8). Brammall draws attention to the fact that the 'romance of quartz' is still causing the miners to ignore the sulphide impregnations (pyrite and arsenopyrite) in shales and that these are potentially valuable ores. However, development continued to concentrate on proving the depth extensions of the quartz reef by cross-cutting from the deeper levels from the shaft and then driving on lode once it had been located (Figure 5.9).

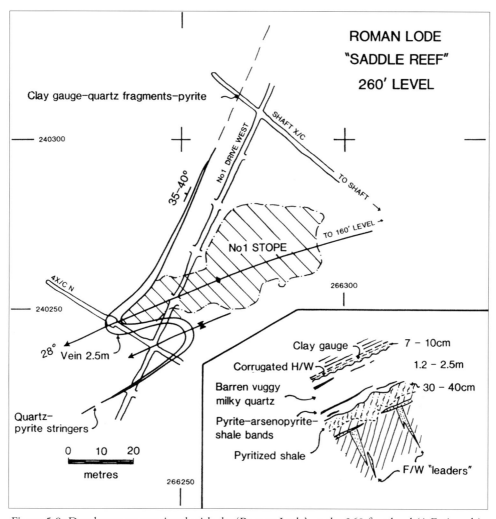

Figure 5.8: Development associated with the 'Roman Lode' on the 260 foot level (A.E. Annels).

Figure 5.9: The 'Roman Lode' exposed on the 260 foot level developed from New Shaft, 1934–5 (Courtesy of the T.R.H. Nelson Collection, Cardiff University).

In March 1936, metallurgical tests on bulk samples revealed that problems existed in the processing of the gold from the milled ore. Over 4% arsenic was found to be present in the material studied, which also contained just under 5 dwt of gold (8 grams per tonne), and that the gold was largely trapped in pyrite and arsenopyrite, representing 13.8% and 10.2% of the ore respectively. Amalgamation, using mercury to extract the gold, was not found to be an efficient process, nor was cyanidation of the raw or roasted ore. Consultants advised flotation of the sulphides and roasting of the concentrates on site, before shipping the product to a custom smelter. It was estimated that the cost of crushing, flotation and roasting would be 5 shillings per ton of ore. This advice, however, was not taken for financial and environmental reasons.

By mid 1936, mine development was well advanced and processing trials on almost 300 tons of development ore shipped to Hamburg had yielded 260 ounces of gold. Over 1,200 metres of exploratory drilling from the 260 foot level, to depths of up to 213 metres, had located payable auriferous intersections, and the future looked bright for the operation. Ore reserves (as defined at the time) were estimated at 150,000 tons assaying 0.25 to 0.5 ounces per ton (8.5 to 17 grams per tonne).

On 6th April 1937 the parent company, Roman Deep Holdings Ltd., formed what they hoped would be the first of several operating companies in Wales. This Company, British Goldfields (No. 1) Ltd., raised £200,000 capital from the sale of two-shilling shares; after the purchase of the lease, surface plant and mining equipment, however, only £44,000 was left as working capital. As it turned out, this was inadequate to sustain the degree of development on the site necessary to produce a viable operation. Mr. Robert Harvey Goodwin was appointed as General Manager, Dr. Alfred Brammall was Consulting Geologist and the directors were Commander A.T.L. Wilson, Admiral A. Bromley, Mr. Harold Edmonds and Captain R.A. Wilson.

Mine development continued apace with the employment of 100 men. A steel headframe was built over the original wooden structure (Figures 5.10 and 5.11), the shaft was extended to 480 feet and cross-cuts were mined on the 360 and 460 foot levels. During 1937, although much

Figure 5.10: New Shaft showing steel headframe built around the earlier wooden structure, 1938
(Industrial and Maritime Museum, National Museum of Wales).

Figure 5.11: Dolaucothi Gold Mine, 1938 (Industrial and Maritime Museum, National Museum of Wales).

Figure 5.12: Advancing the face, 1938 (Courtesy of the T.R.H. Nelson Collection, Cardiff University).

Figure 5.13: The day shift (Courtesy of the T.R.H. Nelson Collection, Cardiff University).

ore had been 'blocked-out' in readiness for stoping, increasingly large amounts of gold were found to be trapped in the sulphides and only minor amounts were recoverable as free particles. Throughout the latter half of the year a new crusher, concentrator and generator house were under construction close to Pen-lan-wen Farm, over a third of a kilometre to the south of the shaft; in January 1938 they were made operational. Details of the processing of the gold ore and the 1938 plant are to be found in Chapter 6 (Figures 5.12 and 5.13).

While development was continuing on the lower levels, most ore production was concentrated on the 100, 160 and 260 foot levels. However, production from the stopes over the 100 foot level ceased at the end of August 1938, as all available ore had been mined out and as the back became 'heavy' (i.e. liable to collapse) and in need of support with 'pig-stys' and timbers. Limited production from this level recommenced in September, exploiting the '100 foot lode' on the north-eastern side of the 'Lead Lode' fault (Figures 3.12 and 5.7). Production from the stopes above the 160 foot level continued at a low rate (5 to 100 tons per week) throughout most of 1938, but the 260 foot level stope was mined out by early April. By the end of this month, production had commenced from the stopes above the 290 foot level (No. 1 and 2 stopes) at an average of 240 tons per week until a deteriorating back caused mining to stop in September. Only limited stoping occurred at the 360 foot level and none is recorded from the 460 foot level. Records are available from 15 weeks between 12th March and 24th September 1938 which show that there was production on only 11 weeks and that this averaged 464 tons per week. The crusher and contractor had been designed with a capacity of 40,000 tons per annum, i.e. approximately 800 tons per week. The mine never met this target with the highest weekly production recorded as 687 tons.

All the stopes referred to were concentrated in a narrow zone, generally less than 25 metres wide, which plunged westwards at an angle of 28° following the nose of the saddle reef at the crest of the anticlinal structure described earlier. The height of the stopes, from hangingwall to footwall, varied from 1.2 metres (the minimum stoping width) to 6 metres, though the reef itself narrowed down to a few centimetres locally.

Figure 5.14 illustrates the method that was employed to extract the ore from between two mining levels. First, a raise would be driven from the lower level to break through into the level above. Occasionally, however, a winze was driven downwards in the opposite direction. In both cases, these were driven so that they followed the dip of the lode, keeping the hangingwall exposed in the top of the advancing face. A similar raise would then be driven on either side, and one or two sub-levels driven horizontally to link them, so subdividing the interval between the two levels into two or three sections. Mining would then take place upwards from each sub-level on either side of the raises using en-echelon bench faces. Pillars would be left to protect the main levels and the ore-chutes in the sub-levels. Ore would be dumped down raises from sub-levels or directly into the main levels via wooden ore-chutes. From here it would be trammed to an ore-pass immediately to the west of the shaft, which in the case of the 100 foot and 160 foot levels penetrated down to the 260 foot level. From here it would be hoisted to the surface in counter-balanced skips and then transferred to tram cars. Two cars, each carrying 3 tons, would be winched up a 30° incline, 280 metres long, to the mill near Pen-lan-wen Farm. This incline was presumably constructed in 1937 but was improved during May 1938 (Figure 5.15). In order to reach the mill, this incline passed through a tunnel 55 metres long beneath the Caio road, before emerging again in the Niagara Pit and then passing through an open cutting 45 metres long, immediately below the tippler station as referred to in Chapter 6 and shown in Figure 6.4.

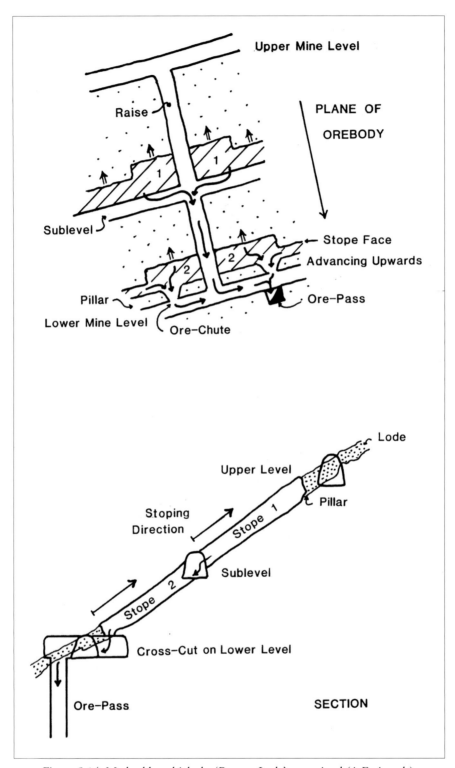

Figure 5.14: Method by which the 'Roman Lode' was mined (A.E. Annels).

At various times during the main production and milling period, January to October 1938, a limited amount of tonnage was gained from Davies Cutting to augment the feed to the mill. Available records suggest that at least 500 tons was obtained from here, although the figure could be as high as 1,000 tons. This was trammed out via the ore-chute and rail track in Mill Adit, which had to be specially lengthened. Also, old dumps around the shaft were reprocessed in an attempt to make up the shortfall to the mill.

Records show that 16,862 tons (17,136 tonnes) of ore were crushed in 1938, a large proportion of which would have been low-grade development ore stockpiled prior to the opening of the mill in January 1938. The value of the gold produced was £11,106, representing a total of 1,388 ounces (43,171 grams) based on the 1938 gold price of £8 per ounce. The grade indicated by these production figures is thus only 2.52 grams per tonnes reflecting the processing of lower-grade development ore; however, as will be seen in Chapter 6, losses to tailings were high so the mill feed grade is likely to have been well in excess of 5 grams per tonne. At 2012 prices (£1,050/oz) and exchange rates (1.62), this gold would have been worth approximately £1.46M (£340,000 in 1995 at the time of the third edition of this book). Over the peak period of production, 200 people were employed in the mine and the mill. However, in November 1938, funds were exhausted and milling ceased. Mr. T.R.H. Nelson, the last Mine Manager, did continue to undertake some exploratory development throughout 1939 and is believed to have begun sinking a new shaft close to the mill site in order to link up directly with Field Adit, with the 160 foot level drive which had looped south-eastwards beneath the Pen-lan-wen workings, and also with the 200 foot level cross-cut south (Figure 5.7). This would have allowed direct hoisting to the mill, as well as exploration of the mineralisation worked in the Niagara and Pen-lan-wen trenches on the surface, and also from underground from the Upper and Lower Roman Adits. Only the concrete shaft collar remains today.

Figure 5.15: Entrance to the incline to the mill on the southern side of the Ogofau Pit, 1938
(Courtesy of the T.R.H. Nelson Collection, Cardiff University).

Figure 5.16: Ogofau Pit showing concrete compressor base and foundations of the 1938–39 mine buildings after demolition c. 1940 (Courtesy of the T.R.H. Nelson Collection, Cardiff University).

Pumping in the mine was stopped in late 1939, after equipment salvage, and final abandonment took place early in 1940, when the buildings were dismantled (Figure 5.16) and 500 lbs of weeping explosives were detonated in a small stope off Long Adit. Both the operating and holding companies were finally dissolved in July 1943.

A study of all the available records for the mine highlights the problems faced by the management in their attempts to launch a profitable enterprise at Dolaucothi. The lack of investment and the geological problems were compounded by the mistakes made in the layout of the shaft and subsequent development levels. We can thus list some of the many features of the operation which made their task an impossible one.

(1) Though the grades were potentially economic, the tonnages of ore available were insufficient to sustain the mill for any prolonged period.

(2) The geological structure of the deposit caused stopes to be small and therefore short-lived.

(3) Rapid fluctuations in thickness and grade of ore took place.

(4) After stopes had been in production for a few months, they suffered from 'heavy backs' resulting in high dilution of ore by the collapse of barren hangingwall (overbreak). Much time was thus spent in setting timber supports or constructing 'pig-stys'.

(5) Bad ground in stopes was also caused by faulting and by the sheared and broken nature of the quartz lodes and associated country rocks.

(6) The gold was increasingly sulphide-locked at depth and was associated with high levels of arsenic (arsenopyrite). Only a small amount could thus be directly recovered on site.

(7) Not enough winzing down to lower levels to prove the location and continuity of the ore at depth prior to cross-cutting from the shaft and subsequent drifting on the lode.

(8) Too much wasted development looking for the lode. On the 260 foot level especially, the drives failed to follow the lode when first located. An attempt to lay out a regular system of drives and cross-cuts meant that the latter had to be excessively long to relocate the lodes.

(9) Initial drives were too small (some were only 1.2 metres high) and had to be slyped to widen them to 2.0 by 1.7 metres to allow tramming operations. Also, many had to be regraded to improve drainage and tramming. Both of these caused inconvenience and additional expense.

(10) Ore- and waste-hoisting facilities were inadequate, a problem compounded by the variable spacing (60 to 100 feet), which made the use of counter-balanced skips/cages difficult. Shaft stations were poorly designed and did not allow easy access to the shaft.

(11) The flat plunge of the ore body to the west required the development of long access cross-cuts in barren ground at the lower mine levels.

(12) Mistakes were made in the initial design of the concentrator in that it was given too high a capacity and attempted to use amalgamation even though this had been proved to be ineffectual by earlier tests.

(13) Because of the presence of high arsenic levels and because of the small tonnages involved, no UK smelter would agree to treat the concentrates. Thus they had to be shipped, at great cost, to Seattle. A proposed contract with a firm in Hamburg was not followed up because of the political situation at the time.

T.R.H. Nelson gives a concise account of the 1933 to 1939 mining operations in a series of papers published in 1944 (see Nelson 1944 in the selected references at the end of the volume). It is clear from these, and other unpublished writings, that he believed the mine to have a future potential and he made recommendations as to how the mine could be rehabilitated and redeveloped to avoid some of the pitfalls which had led to the demise of the last serious attempt to mine the gold ores at Dolaucothi.

Perhaps, one day, more of Dolaucothi's gold will reach the surface.

CHAPTER 6

FROM ORE TO GOLD

INTRODUCTION

In common with his predecessors from the beginning of recorded time, the modern gold producer faces the problem of separating the valuable component from associated material in the mined ore. Although it has been known quite recently for prospectors to discover almost pure gold nuggets as large as footballs, this is exceedingly rare. It is more common, as is the case at Dolaucothi, for the gold to be very finely disseminated and intergrown with troublesome waste (gangue) minerals as discussed earlier in Chapter 3. The problem is to separate the gold from the gangue in the most efficient manner and to dispose of the residue (tailings) safely and economically.

The complexity of the separation processes will depend on the properties of the ore such as the size distribution of the gold and how much of it can be liberated as free gold from the accompanying minerals by grinding alone. Many of the modern techniques are merely refined versions of ones in existence many thousands of years ago. There have, however, been dramatic developments that have revolutionised the processing routes, making the modern plants less dependent on manual labour, more efficient in terms of gold recovery and kinder to the environment.

Although not usually conducted at the mine site, subsequent processes such as refining and alloying with other metals are required before the gold is sold. Purity of gold for the jewellery trade is measured in carats; pure gold being 24 carats. An article of 18 carats would, therefore, contain 18/24th, i.e. 75% gold.

Some facts concerning gold production are worthy of note. Firstly, all of the gold ever produced from 4,000 BC to the present, can be contained in a cube with side approximately equal to the length of a cricket pitch. We are still only adding to the total volume mined of about 9,000m^3, at a rate of about 140m^3 per annum. In 2011, the World Gold Council estimated that more than 60% of the total production has occurred since Dolaucothi closed in 1938. Furthermore, even after the exhaustive efforts to locate, mine and process the metal, most of the gold is still kept in underground vaults and even with the growing demand for gold from industry, e.g. electronics, over three quarters of the current annual production is for decorative or investment purposes.

PROPERTIES OF GOLD AND METHODS USED FOR SEPARATION

Gold is a distinctively yellow, dense, malleable and ductile metal which is virtually indestructible. It is these properties which largely account for its early processing and its ornamental and currency value. One of the simplest early methods for identifying gold was to determine whether the particle had a gritty feel when bitten; gold being softer and smoother than pyrite, commonly known as 'fool's gold'.

After appearance and texture, the next property of gold to be exploited was its high density. In its purest form, it has a density approximately 19 times that of water with a Specific Gravity of approximately 19. Much of the associated gangue, such as quartz, shale and clay, is quite light with a Specific Gravity of 2.6, whereas the sulphides lie predominantly in the Specific Gravity range 4 to 7.5. This high density has been used to separate gold in flowing streams of water using inclined tables, pans, traps, troughs and rocker cradles, or in pulsating currents of water with jigs, and even in currents of air in a fashion similar to winnowing, where water is scarce as in the Australian gold fields.

In the earliest table-washing processes the finely milled ore was placed on an inclined slab where it was sprayed with water which transported the gangue down the slope. The separation was aided by manual agitation of the pulp on the slab and by hand sorting of the coarse gold. After a suitable period, the washing was stopped and the gold remaining on the slab collected and taken for refining. A drawback of this process was that extremely fine material was difficult to treat without excessive loss of gold to tailings. Modern tables work on the same principle but are substantially improved by the development of special decking materials and motion to make the operation continuous. Rotation of cylindrical decks with suitable water injection is a fairly recent development and finds application at many mines for relatively coarse gold recovery.

In a jig, pulsed flows of water are sent through a bed of particles supported in a basket with a perforated base. These pulses can be generated exterior to the bed by means of a plunger, or by simply jigging the basket up and down in a pool of water. The bed stratifies with the higher density particles at the bottom. An advantage of this technique over inclined tabling is that a wider size range of particles can be tolerated in the same machine but extreme fines are again difficult to treat. Since they produce relatively coarse gold, both tables and jigs suffer from a need for strict security.

When gold is contacted with liquid mercury it forms a complex mixture as a result of dissolution, chemical reaction and adhesion. The process is termed amalgamation and this selective removal of gold into a liquid phase has been used extensively in the past. With improved environmental controls it is still used to a lesser extent today. Common practice is to apply amalgamation to the concentrates produced by tables and jigs. The mercury can either be spread on copper plates and the pulp allowed to flow over it, or more commonly today the amalgamation takes place over a period of many hours in a rotating barrel. Amalgam is separated from the gangue by settling and washing with water. It is then heated slowly at first, to vaporise the mercury, then at a higher temperature, to drive off impurities and melt the gold. Mercury is recovered by condensing the fumes from the furnace. The gold must be free in order for the amalgamation to be successful. It is, therefore, not suitable for gold trapped within sulphide or other minerals.

Towards the end of the 19th century it was discovered that gold, which was thought to be immune from chemical attack other than by such strong acids as mixtures of nitric and hydrochloric acids (aqua regia), could be dissolved in cyanide solutions under comparatively mild operating conditions. The cyanide process is now almost universally adopted wherever gold is produced. The dissolution mechanism is still a subject for research but it is commonly accepted to be an electrochemical process requiring constant agitation and the presence of dissolved oxygen.

Each application of this process has its own peculiarities but basically the sequence begins with the addition of sodium or potassium cyanide to an aqueous alkaline slurry of finely ground ore. The pulp is then agitated by bubbling air into large vats for periods ranging from one to several days. Classically the gold is recovered by adding zinc, after first removing the solid gangue by filtration. The gold precipitate is finally recovered by filtration and refined by smelting. The method can be costly especially if a very fine grind is necessary for gold liberation.

An alternative modern development, not available to the 1930s operators, is to absorb the gold-cyanide complex onto activated charcoal particles (coconut charcoal is particularly suitable) which are large enough to be removed from the pulp by screening. The process is conducted in a series of tanks with the charcoal moving counter-current to the pulp, i.e. fresh charcoal contacts the most dilute auro-cyanide solution which makes for the most efficient gold removal. Loaded charcoal can either go directly for smelting or can be stripped of gold by washing with hot, strong alkaline cyanide solution from which the gold is removed by electroplating. The charcoal can then be returned to the process after reactivation by heating. This so called 'carbon-in-pulp' process is particularly suitable for carbonaceous ores that have proved difficult to treat by the classical cyanidation route.

Some minerals have a stronger affinity for air than for water. If small air bubbles are introduced into a slurry containing a mixture of such hydrophobic minerals and others which are hydrophilic, then the hydrophobic components can be floated to the surface and skimmed off in the froth which forms there. This forms the basis for the process referred to as 'froth flotation' which revolutionised metal production from ores in the 20th century. In modern plants it is common to add chemicals which selectively render certain minerals hydrophobic and which improve froth formation. Gold, or more precisely, the sulphide containing locked gold particles, can be separated from the gangue in this way, thus allowing separations at particle sizes much lower than could be treated by tabling or jigging.

There are various routes available for extracting the gold from the sulphide concentrates depending on whether the gold can be liberated by further grinding and whether the sulphides are harmful to cyanidation. If the latter is the case then the sulphide can either be roasted prior to dissolution or sent for gold recovery by the pyro-metallurgical technique of smelting. A novel approach involves the use of bacteria (*Thiobacillus ferro-oxidens*) to oxidise the sulphides prior to cyanidation. This so-called 'bacterial leaching' process takes longer than roasting, but involves milder reaction conditions and fewer environmental problems.

GOLD PROCESSING AT DOLAUCOTHI

(a) Early ore processing

The recognition and interpretation of early processing sites at Dolaucothi remains an under-researched field, further complicated by the impact of later mining activities. Although it is known that the Romans possessed the technology to treat gold in association with sulphides, early miners in Wales were primarily concerned with free gold. Prevailing mining techniques essentially limited their activities to mineralised zones close to surface where natural weathering processes had largely decomposed the sulphides and, as a result, liberated the gold.

Evidence for early ore processing has now been recovered from various parts of the mine complex. Where hard-rock deposits were present, the concentration process is likely to have commenced by hand sorting ('cobbing') the high-grade material, which then had to be crushed and ground using large pestles and mortars and rotary quern-stones similar to those employed for flour milling. Several examples of such stones are known from the vicinity of Ogofau Lodge, including one fragment from the site of the 1991–93 excavations. It has also been suggested in Chapter 4 that the nearby Carreg Pumsaint may be associated with the remains of a water-driven, trip-hammer mill of a type not hitherto known from Roman contexts (Figure 4.12). Though its identification is not without its problems, it reinforces the possibility that water power could have been used to facilitate the crushing process, besides its more familiar role in the processing of the crushed ore.

Following crushing and grinding, the finely milled ore would have been washed using a controlled stream of water which was readily available from the different leat systems. Evidence for this can perhaps be seen in the offset gulley below Tank C, on the south-eastern side of the Mitchell Pit, which has been interpreted as a set of three rock-cut steps or washing tables (Figure 6.1). Water would have been supplied from the Tank via a sluice gate, the remains of which were discovered during excavations in 1969–70. Though these steps could have supported a set of inclined wooden washing tables, it is more likely that the broken character of the local shale would have sufficed to trap the heavier gold particles while the lighter gangue minerals were washed away downslope; the gold would have been recovered later by sweeping, once the steps had dried out. This gravity precipitation of gold could also have been aided by the use of branches of gorse laid facing upstream on these steps. These would not only have created turbulence to assist in the separation of the gold particles, but would also have trapped very fine gold (flour) in its leaves. This could have been recovered by burning the charged branches. Amalgamation and/or smelting might then have been used as further concentration steps.

Such a cascade system is likely to have had a limited life and realistically could only have processed ore from the Mitchell Pit. Its location is totally unsuitable for processing the ore from the much larger Ogofau Pit, for instance, which must surely have been processed downslope from the workings rather than uphill. The limited amount of tailings produced from this site

Figure 6.1: Stepped washing tables below Tank C; the 1-metre scales mark the boundaries between the steps (B.C. Burnham).

would most probably have been deposited in the area now occupied by Melin-y-Milwyr, whence some of it might have been transported further away by the stream occupying the saddle between Allt Cwmhenog and Allt Ogofau. Though this stream now flows down into the Ogofau Pit, disappearing beneath the waste fill of this pit, it is possible that in the earliest phases of mining it flowed south-eastwards in the opposite direction towards the river Annell in the next valley. This is suggested by a plume of arsenic contamination in the alluvial sediments here which is unrelated to bedrock mineralisation.

P.R. Lewis has recently suggested that two water-filled reservoirs, now known as Melin-y-Milwyr, might have formed part of another cascade system on the basis of some Roman pottery discovered in the outer clay wall of the upper pond in the 1970s; stone culverts are also described as linking these reservoirs to one another and to the Ogofau Pit below. Though Roman processing in the area cannot be discounted, the current size and configuration of the reservoirs clearly represent the product of later mining: the lower pond, for instance, was utilised by a small mill, which was powered by a water wheel established there in the early 1870s; while its larger counterpart above acted as a silting pond, which was located immediately below the walls of the dam built to contain tailings from the 1938 plant on the hillside above. Arguably, both ponds were refurbished in the 1930s, in order to catch slimes being carried down-stream from the water-logged tailings. It is, therefore, unlikely that any of the Roman pottery (and some 17th-century material) was *in situ*, having been incorporated into the dam during one of its phases of refurbishment.

The suggestion by D.G. Bird that the Romans exploited areas of relatively soft and weathered pyritic shale by the extensive use of water for ground-sluicing raises the distinct possibility that the resulting debris would have been collected and processed in channels or sluices located at the foot of the mine workings. This might help to explain several linear gullies which have been identified on the flood-plain below the workings and for the plume of arsenic contamination which extends out into the Cothi valley and is evidently derived from the Allt Cwmhenog opencast. It might also account for the crushed quartz found during ploughing in the fields north of Ogofau Lodge and for the sedimented beds of crushed material recorded at the Lodge itself, both of which are probably the result of large-scale washing activities. Excavations near the Carreg Pumsaint in 1991–93 revealed the presence of further tailings, the microscopic examination of which demonstrated that they comprised crushed quartz and crystals of pyrite now completely oxidised by circulating groundwaters.

Irrespective of the different methods involved, one of the surprising features of the site is the apparent lack of tailings and waste rock commensurate with the known extent of the mine workings. While much of the finely crushed tailings might have entered the river Cothi, thence to be washed downstream or reworked by later operators, the evidence known from the vicinity of the Ogofau Lodge emphasises that a study of the outwash areas on the floodplain remains an urgent priority. Large dumps of waste rock might also be expected to be present close to the mine but, apart from the material forming the makeup of the so-called motte and its immediate surroundings, surprisingly little is recognisable today. Some might have been transported away for use as foundation material over the intervening centuries, as it certainly was after World War II from the area of the modern car-park below the mine; some must also have been used as backfill in the Ogofau Pit, prior to the commencement of the 19th- and 20th-century mining operations. Clearly this is an area where further work is needed.

Knowing the limitation of recovery efficiency on inclined tables and the fine dissemination of gold at Dolaucothi, it is probable that much of the gold mined was lost to tailings. For the Romans, the operation was probably only 'profitable' as a result of the cheap conscript or convict labour.

(b) Processing in the 19th and early 20th centuries

There is very little documented evidence concerning the processing of ore at Dolaucothi during this period. Location and description of the processing sites is indeed still a matter under investigation. What is known is that several groups of miners attempted gold extraction towards the end of the 19th century and the remains of a site dated to c. 1888 can still be seen near the eastern extremity of the Ogofau Pit (Figure 6.2). One such group of Australian miners conducted a small operation where they crushed the ore in stamp mills which were capable of reducing

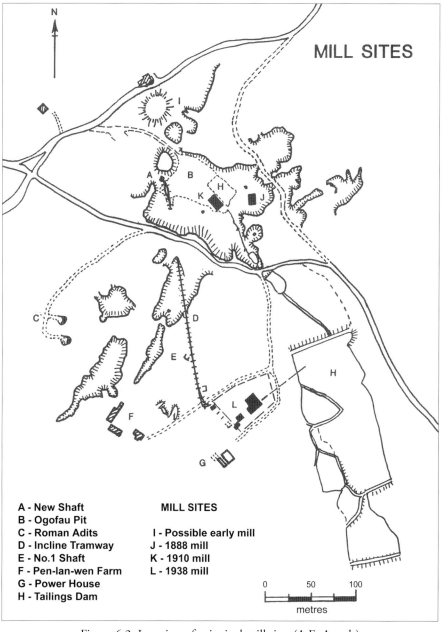

Figure 6.2: Location of principal mill sites (A.E. Annels).

relatively coarse material to powder in one operation. Free gold was recovered by gravity techniques and possibly amalgamation. Panning of waste material in the bed of the stream adjacent to Davies Cutting has revealed the presence of globules of mercury which either relate to the use of this method in the early 1870s or to the early days of the 1938 mill when this method was used despite recommendations as to its unsuitability made at the time. Because stamps work best on hard rocks it is likely that they processed ore from quartz leaders close to the surface. Gold concentrations would have been low (approximately 3 grams per tonne) and, when it is considered that the stamp could crush at most a few tonnes per day, the operation must have been marginal.

During the period 1905–1910 most of the processing took place in a mill located within the south-eastern corner of the Ogofau Pit near Mill Adit (Figures 5.16 and 6.2). A rolls crusher and jigs were used to produce a primary sulphide concentrate which assayed at between 50 and about 200 grams per tonne of gold. The tailings were deposited in the eastern half of the Ogofau Pit where they infill the base of the Roman excavation to depths of several metres. Unfortunately no smelter would offer reasonable terms for gold extraction because of the high arsenic content. Direct amalgamation on site proved unsuccessful and insufficient capital was available to erect the necessary smelting facilities at Dolaucothi.

Few records of the processing operations in this period exist but the report of a trial milling on 70 tonnes of ore with an average gold grade of 12 grams per tonne suggests that about 30% of the gold was lost to tailings if concentration was by gravity techniques alone. It is rather surprising, therefore that the prime concentrating device used in the next mill to be erected on site was a table, a gravity-based process.

(c) The 1930s Mill

The processing operations during the last period of mining are well documented, thanks to a series of articles by the former mine manager, T.R.H. Nelson (see Nelson 1944 in the selected references at the end of the volume). The mill was situated on the hillside about 300 metres to the south of the present Ogofau Pit near Pen-lan-wen farm (Figures 6.3 to 6.5).

Figure 6.6 summarises the stages in the processing of the ore during the final months of the life of the plant. Initially the ground ore from the ball mill was passed over inclined blanket tables. These trapped the largest grains of gold and the coarser sulphides which were then contacted with mercury in the amalgamation barrel. Losses of gold to the tailings as trapped particles in sulphides were unacceptably high, although not surprising, when it is considered what problems had beset earlier attempts at gold recovery. Similar techniques had failed some 30 years before, and various more recent consultancy reports on the processing of the ores had predicted that this would happen. The plan was thus quickly modified so that the fine slurry passed, via a centrifugal classifier, to froth-flotation cells (Figure 6.7) which produced an auriferous sulphide concentrate. The tailings then passed to the tailings dam in the valley bottom (Figures 6.2 and 6.8). This modification should have allowed the processing of the ores at a rate of 100 to 150 tonnes per hour, but as has been described in Chapter 5, the mine was unable to satisfy the demand. Sadly, the plant only operated for nine months over the period February to October 1938, and only in September did the mine meet its call and the plant operate at a profit (4,800 tonnes milled for a recovery of 30 kilograms of gold). This was only possible because they were able to treat a stockpile of probably low-grade development ore, material from Davies Cutting, old waste dumps and probably also tailings discarded earlier in the year. G.W. Hall reports that overall the plant

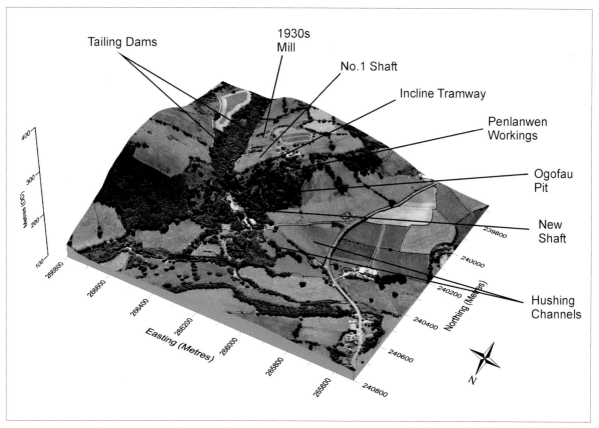

Figure 6.3: 3D topographic map showing the location of the 1930s mill in relation to New Shaft
(P.J. Brabham, Cardiff University).

Figure 6.4: Inclined tramway, winder house, tippler station and collar of No. 1 shaft, 1938
(Mine and Quarry Journal, 1944).

Figure 6.5: The 1938 mill complex (Mine and Quarry Journal 1944).

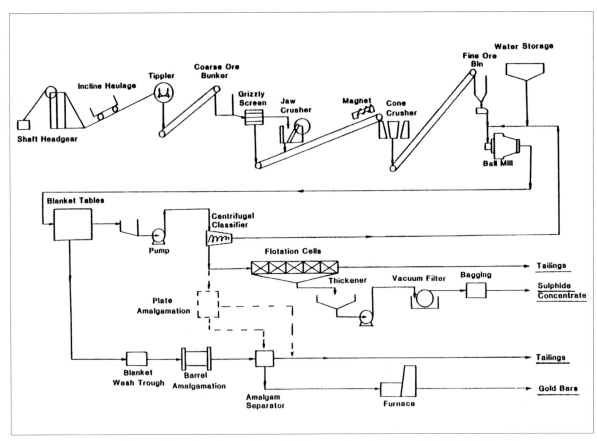

Figure 6.6: Simplified flow sheet of the gold plant on Pen-lan-wen, 1938 (K.P. Williams).

Figure 6.7: A bank of froth-flotation cells producing a
sulphide concentrate (Mine and Quarry Journal, 1944).

Figure 6.8: The tailings dam below the 1938 mill (Mine and Quarry Journal, 1944).

produced 1,388 oz (approximately 43 Kg) of gold from 16,862 tons (17,133 tonnes) of ore in 1938. This is equivalent to 2.52 grams per tonne.

In 1972, an extensive investigation of the tailings pond left by the 1938 operations was performed by the then Department of Mineral Exploitation at University College, Cardiff (Figure 6.9). This confirmed earlier estimates of the total ore milled to be about 20,000 tonnes, which indicates that over its short life this plant was operating at no more than 60% capacity, a deplorable situation considering the high capital expenditure. Boreholes in the tailings dam revealed that the average grade of gold there was in excess of 2 grams per tonne. This, on the basis of predictions of the grade of the mill feed, indicates that the overall recovery was less than 65%. This is unacceptably low when levels of 90 to 95% could be obtained using the appropriate technology.

A more detailed investigation of the tailings dam was undertaken during 1997 and 1998 in order to confirm the tonnage and grade of the tailings. An initial hand auger sampling programme in 1997 had limited success so this was followed up in 1998 by a vibrocorer drilling programme (Figure 6.10A) during which 14 holes were drilled. All penetrated the full thickness into a layer of peat and clay representing the pre-tailings valley floor. Thicknesses encountered varied from 0.7 to 3.6 metres.

Associated geophysical studies using Ground-Probing Radar and Electrical imaging (Figure 6.10B) confirmed that the maximum thickness of tailings sediments in the dam varies over the valley profile, but the maximum thickness is less than 4 metres (Figure 6.11). The results of this surveying programme demonstrate that the surface area of the 1938 tailings dam is 5,430m^2 and that the total volume of tailings sediments is around 10,500m^3. This volume equates to 21,000 tonnes of wet sediment equivalent to 16,800 tonnes of dry material. This is very close to that quoted earlier confirming this tonnage estimate.

A total of 93 samples were taken at a variety of depths in all 14 holes and analysed for Arsenic (AS), Iron (Fe) and Manganese (MN) by XRF techniques. A subset of 22 samples was also sent for gold assay. The latter showed a good linear correlation between arsenic concentration and gold grade though, at gold levels exceeding 4,000ppm, the relationship changed and gold concentrations were significantly higher than would have been predicted by the use of a regression equation established for arsenic levels below 4,000ppm. This might suggest that in lower-grade samples the gold is largely trapped within arsenopyrite but in the high-grade samples the sulphide locked gold grade is augmented by free gold. It is noticeable that the highest arsenic levels are close to the decant point of the tailings slurry into the tailings dam reflecting the early gravity settling of heavy sulphide particles near this pipe outlet.

The average gold grade returned from the 22 samples was 2.68ppm (grams per tonne). However, if the linear relationship between gold and arsenic, as expressed in a mathematical equation, is applied to the larger dataset (excluding two very high values and one from peat), then the average grade is 3.00ppm (grams per tonne).

Though the historically recovered gold grade reported earlier was only 2.52 grams per tonne additional gold would have reported to sulphide concentrates produced by froth flotation. If only 5% of the ore contained sulphide then this represents over 800 tonnes of concentrate but unfortunately its grade is not known as the mine was unable to find a smelter willing or able to process this material. Given the grades reported above for the tailings, it is evident that the 65% recovery of both free and sulphide locked gold is probably realistic.

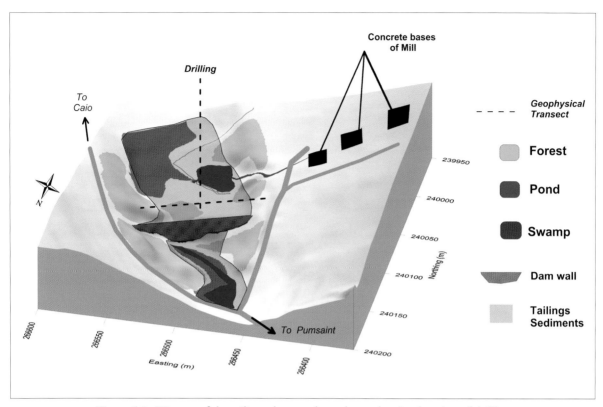

Figure 6.9: 3D map of the tailings dams and pond area showing location of drilling
(P.J. Brabham, Cardiff University).

Figure 6.10: A) Vibrocoring and sampling of the tailings sediments (May 1998);
B) Geophysical Ground Probing Radar survey carried out by Dr. Jonathan Thomas of Terradat (UK) Ltd.
(June 1998) (P.J. Brabham, Cardiff University).

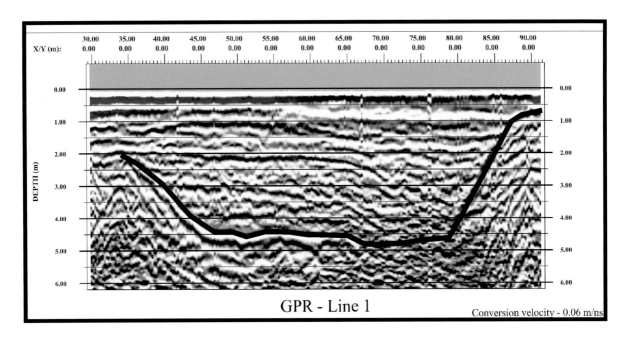

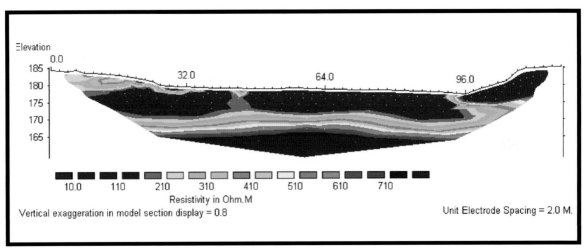

Figure 6.11: Results of the geophysical transects across the tailings dam sediments:
Top – Ground-Probing Radar survey; Bottom – Electrical Resistivity image of the tailings sediment
(P.J. Brabham, Cardiff University).

If an average grade of 3 grams per tonne is accepted for the 16,800 dry tonnes of tailings then this represents a gold content of 50.4 kg. At a 2013 stock exchange gold price of £33,800 per kg, this equates to an *in-situ* value of £1.7 million. However, a large proportion of this gold is likely to be locked in arsenopyrite thus making it environmentally difficult and expensive to liberate.

CONCLUSION

Throughout the long life of the Dolaucothi Mine the efficiency of gold recovery has been low. An appreciable proportion of the gold mined was lost in tailings, much of it locked in sulphide minerals. With the passage of time a large percentage of these sulphides will have been removed by natural dissolution processes aided by the presence of bacteria, thus leaving the gold amenable to modern recovery techniques. However, most of the mining waste has been widely scattered and possibly washed away in the river Cothi where the first traces of gold in this locality may well have been found in pre-Roman times.

Chapter 7

CONCLUSION

The Dolaucothi Gold Mines have been of great interest to many generations of people starting first with the miners who exploited the site from the earliest times through to the 19th and 20th centuries, and continuing more recently with the archaeologists, geologists and mining engineers who have explored the site from the 1960s onwards. Visitors to the gold mines since the early 1980s have also been able to learn about the gold deposits and how they were mined, both from the information provided by the National Trust guides and from reading previous editions of this book following their visit.

The third edition of this book was published in 1995, since when significant new research has been undertaken, incorporating new surveys, techniques and instrumentation, to develop our knowledge of the gold mines and life in the area of Pumsaint. This Revised New Edition of *The Dolaucothi Gold Mines – Geology and Mining History*, brings the story up to date and will hopefully be of interest to visitors who have a specialist or general knowledge of gold mining or of the Dolaucothi story in particular.

The results of the geochemical, geophysical and drilling investigations conducted by Cardiff University staff since 1974 have identified the main types and modes of origin of gold mineralisation in the Dolaucothi area. Mineralogical studies show that arsenic is the main identifying element for gold and is closely related to the sulphide mineral arsenopyrite. The main sources of gold ore may be summarised as occurring in the following: pyritic shales within the cores of isoclinal anticlines, pyritised shale beds, a conformable quartz saddle reef, and planar veins extending down below the saddle reef. The gold-bearing zone has been recorded as being up to 1.25 kilometres in length, although within this zone the gold ore occurs in discontinuous pockets. It is possible that further exploration could extend its length. While a significant understanding exists about the origin and extent of the gold deposits, further studies, based primarily on a comprehensive drilling programme, could provide added information such as the depth and level of ore reserves that still exist at the gold mines, a point of much interest to visitors.

Archaeological research, first by staff of Manchester University from 1960 to 1975 and then from the University of Wales, Lampeter from the 1980s onwards, has done much to explore the evidence for early mining, emphasising in the process that water power played an important part in the exploration, extraction and processing of the gold ore deposits through a system of leat channels and associated reservoirs. Much of this activity has traditionally been assigned to the Roman period, reflecting the importance of the nearby Roman fort and its associated settlements. Many of the archaeological conclusions about the early mining are, however, interpretations of the surviving features of the site and it remains possible that both pre-historic and medieval/post medieval mining may also have taken place. As in the case of the present geological knowledge, further exploration within the opencasts, along the line of the leat systems and in the associated processing areas would do much to clarify this and add to the general archaeological attraction of the site. This may be of special significance with the current emphasis being given to the Roman period and activities in this area of south-west Wales.

It would appear that the total amount of gold mined at Dolaucothi over pre-Roman, Roman and modern times does not compare with that obtained from the Dolgellau mines of the 19th century. However, the Dolaucothi Gold Mines have several advantages: they are still very accessible today and in the ownership of the National Trust and they possess the added attraction of the lure of gold and an insatiable interest in the Roman period in Wales.

It is for such reasons that visitor access has been so successful since 1983, with visits by people from all parts of the UK and from Europe. Visits by school parties, symposia and the general public have raised the general awareness of the geology and mining history of a unique gold mine.

In the present era of conservation and collaboration between national and international bodies such as the European Union, the Welsh Government, the National Trust and Welsh Universities, it is to be hoped that more about Dolaucothi's gold will reach the ears of a continuing flow of visitors. The educational and aesthetic qualities of this site of outstanding natural beauty in south-west Wales will ensure much interest and enjoyment for future generations.

GLOSSARY

Adit: A horizontal tunnel into the hillside.

Actinolite: A calcium, magnesium iron silicate mineral, pale green to viridian green in colour.

Alluvial: Sediments or mineral deposits formed by river transport and deposition.

Amalgamation: The process by which gold in the crushed ore is combined with mercury. The amalgam sinks to the bottom of the retainer and the light sandy material is washed away.

Ankerite: An iron and magnesium bearing carbonate mineral (very pale brown).

Anticline: An arch-shaped fold in the rock.

Auriferous veins: Quartz veins containing minute grains of gold.

Back: The roof of a stope or tunnel.

Ball Mill: Rotating cylindrical vessel part-filled with broken rock and also by hard steel balls which produce finely ground material by impact.

'Blocked-out' ore: Ore for which mine development is complete and is ready for exploitation. It is also fully proved by underground sampling.

Britten Pan: An amalgamation pan used for the recovery of gold and silver from crushed ores.

Calcite: Calcium carbonate (white).

Cambrian: The geological period from 600 to 519 million years ago.

Chlorite: An iron and magnesium bearing silicate mineral (green).

Colluvial: Surficial deposits formed by *in-situ* chemical weathering and erosion.

Concordant: Lying in the same plane as the surrounding host rocks.

Conformable: Strata that lie on top of one another in regular order.

Cornish Rolls: A crushing device consisting of counter-rotating iron cylinders. The ore is fed into the gap between the cylinders and crushed in the process.

Cross-cut: A mine tunnel which cuts across the general geological strike of the rocks or the ore body.

Crust: Outer shell of the Earth.

Cyanidation:	The process by which gold and silver are taken into solution in water containing potassium or sodium cyanide. This occurs under oxygenated conditions.
Deleterious elements:	Chemical elements which can have an adverse effect on metallurgical processes or on the environment.
Dip:	Maximum inclination of a plane to the horizontal.
Drive:	A tunnel which follows the strike of an ore body, either within ore or in the immediate host rocks.
Dwt:	A pennyweight, which represents 1/20 of a troy ounce of gold. 1 troy ounce = 31.1 grams.
Electroplating:	Removal of metal from solution by deposition onto a charged electrode.
Epidote:	A calcium aluminium silicate mineral, apple green in colour.
Exsolution bleb:	Material which was originally incorporated in the parent mineral but which, on cooling, was rejected and formed tiny blebs scattered throughout the host mineral.
Fault:	A break in the continuous mass of rock attended by movement on one side or the other of the break.
Fire-setting:	A mining technique using fires to heat the rock face, thereby inducing large stresses which cause the rock to shatter.
Footwall:	The lower enclosing wall of an inclined vein - footwall rocks are thus those lying vertically beneath the ore body/vein.
Froth Flotation:	Process of mineral concentration by attachment of hydrophobic particles to air bubbles and collection in a semi-stable froth.
Gangue:	Minerals which occur with the ore but which have no value in their own right.
Ground-sluicing:	A mining technique which involves directing a powerful stream of water from a reservoir onto a soft ore deposit, in order to fragment and break it up; the resulting debris is thereby carried downhill into channels or sluices where any gold can be separated from the waste rock.
Grs:	Abbreviation for grain, which is 1/24 of one pennyweight (dwt).
Hangingwall:	The upper surface of a vein or ore body. Also the rocks overlying an ore body.
Hushing:	A mining technique which involves the release of a substantial body of water downslope from a reservoir in order to clear away the overburden and so expose the solid geology and any viable ore deposits. It is primarily used as a prospecting technique during the early stages of

exploration, but can also be used when any workings are subsequently extended to new areas.

Hydraulicing: A mining technique which involves directing a jet of water under high pressure onto an ore deposit, with the intention of fragmenting it and washing the resulting debris downslope into wooden troughs where any gold can be extracted. It is usually applied in modern contexts post-dating the mid-19th century, though it has sometimes been loosely used at Dolaucothi as a general term for all water-assisted (hydraulic) mining.

Hydromorphic: A chemical dispersion produced by solution into, and transport by, surface waters.

Hydromuscovite: A white mica (more precisely the clay illite).

Hydrophilic: Water loving, difficult to attach to air bubbles in froth flotation.

Hydrophobic: Water hating, easily attached to air bubbles in froth flotation.

Igneous activity: Intrusion of molten rock (magma) into the Earth's crust.

Isoclinal: Both limbs of a fold dip in the same direction.

Jig: A device for agitating a bed of crushed ore in water so that the heavier sulphides and gold sink to the bottom.

Leach: Dissolution of certain components of the ore or rock.

Lode zone: A belt of rocks which has been invaded by hot fluids (hydrothermal solutions) from which quartz, carbonate, gold and metallic sulphides (e.g. pyrite) have been precipitated.

LIDAR: Stands for **L**aser **I**maging **D**etection and **R**anging. This is an optical remote sensing technology that can measure the distance to, or other properties of, targets by illuminating the target with laser light and analysing the backscattered light.

Lithology/lithological: The type of rock present/relating to rock type.

Metamorphism: A change in texture or composition of a rock by such agencies as heat, moisture and pressure.

Micron: One thousandth part of a millimetre.

Mineral: A rock substance of regular and definite chemical composition.

Motte: A circular, steep-sided, flat-topped earthen mound of Norman date, surrounded by a wide ditch and surmounted by a timber fortification.

Nodule: A small round aggregate of mineral grains often with a concentric or radial internal structure.

Ordovician: The geological period from 519 to 438 million years ago.

Ore: Mineralised rock which could be mined at a profit.

Orogeny: Mountain-building event when the initially flat-lying rocks were folded, faulted and uplifted.

Outcrop: Surface exposure of a rock.

Placer deposits: Mineral deposits formed by river action – heavier particles are concentrated in hollows in the bed of the stream/river.

'Pig Sty': A timber pack used to support the roof of a stope.

Pillow mounds: Distinctive low rectangular mounds with shallow side ditches, often found in clusters, which represent artificial rabbit warrens.

Pyritised: Rock that has been extensively replaced by pyrite.

Raise: An inclined shaft driven up the dip of the lode from a lower level.

Reef: Flat-lying or concordant tabular body of quartz.

Regression equation: An equation which expresses the mathematical relationship between two variables such as arsenic and gold; in the case of a linear relationship then this would be in the form y=mx+c where y and x are the variables under study, m is the slope of the line and c is the intercept above the origin of the graph.

Reverse fault: Like thrusts (which are flat-lying) reverse faults have been produced by compression in the Earth's crust so that the block of rock overlying a steeply dipping fault plane has been moved upwards over the underlying block.

Saddle reef: A quartz vein intruded into a fold structure so that it has a saddle-like shape with the thickest section corresponding to the crest of the fold.

Siderite: An iron carbonate which rapidly oxidises to a dark reddish brown colour.

Sill: A body of igneous rock intruded parallel to the bedding of the sedimentary rock (e.g. shales, sandstones).

Silurian: The geological period from 438 to 400 million years ago.

Skip: A large bucket-like container used to hoist ore or waste rock to the surface.

Slimes: Very fine muddy material produced during the milling of ore; largely clay but in this instance could include some carbonaceous material.

Slype: To widen a tunnel.

Stamp mill: A crushing device consisting of heavy vertical rods which are mechanically lifted and dropped onto the ore often with the aid of water power.

Stope (verb to stope): The hole underground from which ore has, or is being, extracted. The verb represents the process of removal of ore from the stope.

Strike:	A horizontal line drawn on a plane at right angles to the direction of dip.
Stringers:	A network of thin veinlets often with random orientation and irregular form.
Syncline:	A trough-shaped fold.
Table:	Mineral-concentrating device where particles are separated in a flowing stream of water on an inclined deck. Earlier models (Strake) had stationary decks with a wide range of coverings (blankets, wood, linoleum, corduroy, velvet). Modern versions (Wilfley) use a shaking motion.
Tailings:	Fine material from which the valuable constituents have been removed.
Tectonic subsidence:	Collapse of the ground due to movements in the Earth's crust.
Tectonised zone:	A corridor of rock which has been subjected to intense shearing, fracturing, deformation and fragmentation.
Thrust:	A flat lying fracture in the Earth's crust along which movement has taken place so that the overlying block has ridden over the lower.
Tippler station:	Here tram cars from the mine were tipped sideways to discharge their load via a chute onto a conveyor belt feeding coarse ore bins.
Tuff:	Volcanic ash which may be deposited on land or in bodies of water.
Vibrocorer:	A hand-held drill which, using a petrol engine, can drive a core barrel up to 10 metres into the ground via a vibratory action. Suitable only for soft overburden.
Vein/veinlets:	A fissure or fracture that has been infilled with minerals, usually quartz, calcite and metallic sulphides, deposited from cooling hot fluids migrating up from depth in the Earth's crust.
Vuggy:	Full of cavities, i.e. vughs.
Winze:	An inclined shaft driven down the dip of the lode from an upper level.
XRF:	**X R**ay **F**luorescence.

Selected references

Agricola, G. 1556, *De Re Metallica* (1950 English Edition, translated by H.C. & L.H. Hoover), New York.

Annels, A.E. 1984, Exploration for gold in Wales, *Chartered Land Surveyor/ Chartered Minerals Surveyor (RICS)* 2, No. 12.

Annels, A.E. & Roberts, D.E. 1989, Turbidite-hosted gold mineralization at the Dolaucothi Gold Mines, Dyfed, Wales, United Kingdom, *Economic Geology* 84, 1293–314.

Bick, D. 1989, An ancient leat near Dolaucothi gold mine, *Archaeology in Wales* 28 (1988), 20–1.

Bird, D.G. 2001, Aspects of Roman gold-mining: Dolaucothi, Asturias and Pliny, in Higham, N.J. (ed.) *Archaeology of the Roman Empire: a Tribute to the Life and Works of Professor Barri Jones*, BAR International Series 940, Oxford, 265–75.

Boon, G.C. & Williams, C. 1966, The Dolaucothi drainage wheel, *Journal of Roman Studies* 56, 122–7.

Briggs, C.S. 2009, Some preliminary observations on Sir John Gardner Wilkinson's survey of the Ogofau Gold Mines, Dolaucothi, of 1868, in James, H. & Moore, P. (ed.), *Carmarthenshire and Beyond: Studies in History and Archaeology in Memory of Terry James*, Carmarthenshire Antiquarian Society, 134–49.

Burnham, B.C. & Burnham H.B. 2004, *Dolaucothi-Pumsaint: Survey and Excavations at a Roman Gold-Mining Complex, 1987-1999*, Oxford: Oxbow Books.

Burnham, B.C. & Hopewell, D. 2012, Recent Geophysical Survey at the Roman Fort of Pumsaint, 2011, *Archaeology in Wales* 51 (2011), 121–6.

Davies, O. 1936, Finds at Dolaucothi, *Archaeologia Cambrensis* 91, 51–7.

Hall, G.W. 1988, A suggested solution to some problems of the Dolaucothi gold mines site, South Wales, *Archaeology in Wales* 27 (1987), 67.

Hall, G.W. 1993, *Metal Mines of Southern Wales* (2nd edition), Kington.

Holman, B.W. 1911, Gold Deposits of Cothy, South Wales, *Mining Magazine,* May, 374–8.

Howell, R. 1991, *Dolaucothi Education Project: The Romans. A History-Based Topic Pack*, Llandeilo: National Trust.

Isaac, A.K. 2012, *Dolaucothi Gold: A Vision Realised. The Restoration and Development of an old Roman Gold Mine*, Caerleon: Apecs Press.

Isaac, M.R. 1991, *Dolaucothi Education Project: Welsh Legend and Culture. A Literature-Based Topic Pack*, Llandeilo: National Trust.

Jones, G.D.B., Blakey, I.J. & Macpherson, E.C.F. 1960, Dolaucothi: the Roman aqueduct, *Bulletin of the Board of Celtic Studies* 19, 71–84.

Jones, G.D.B. & Lewis, P.R. 1971, The Dolaucothi Gold-mines, *Bönner Jahrbücher* 171, 288–300.

Lewis, M.J.T. 1997, *Millstone and Hammer: the Origins of Water Power,* University of Hull.

Lewis, P.R. 1977, The Ogofau Roman Gold Mines at Dolaucothi, *National Trust Yearbook 1976-77,* 16pp.

Lewis, P.R. & Jones, G.D.B. 1969, The Dolaucothi Gold Mines 1: The surface evidence, *Archaeological Journal* 49, 244–72.

Murchison, R.I. 1839, *The Silurian System,* London.

Nelson, T.R.H. 1944, Gold mining in south Wales, *Mine and Quarry Engineering* 9, Jan, Feb, March issues, 3–10, 33–38, 55–60.

Smyth, W.W. 1846, Note on the Gogofau or Ogofau mine near Pumsaint, Carmarthenshire, *Memoirs of the Geological Survey* (1846), 480–4.